AN INTRODUCTION TO
STAINLESS STEEL

J. Gordon Parr
University of Windsor
Windsor, Ontario, Canada
and
Albert Hanson
Hanson Materials Engineering, Ltd.
Edmonton, Alberta, Canada

AMERICAN SOCIETY FOR METALS
Metals Park, Ohio

Distributor outside the United States and Canada:
Chapman & Hall, Limited
11 New Fetter Lane
London EC4, England

First Printing, 1966
Second Printing, 1971

Library of Congress Catalog Card Number:
65-27458

Printed in the United States of America

Preface

"Stainless steel" is a generic term covering a large group of alloys. Commonly known for their corrosion resistance, these steels also exhibit a large range of other useful properties, the divergence of which can only be understood after the constitution and treatment are examined in an orderly fashion.

Such examination is the purpose of this book. The stainless steels are categorized, the reasons why each category has special properties are studied, and the properties themselves are enumerated. Methods of fabrication and heat treatment are considered on the same basis. Naturally, the mechanism and the achievement of corrosion resistance are also considered.

Because this is an introductory book, no pretense of including all information on stainless steels is made. Nevertheless, adequate data are presented to make this book a convenient basic reference once the reader has become acquainted with this group of steels.

It is our hope that this book will be understood by anyone engaged in the use or study of metals. So that the body of the book will not fail through a reader's lack of familiarity with metallurgical principles, a short introduction to the general subject is offered in Chapter 3. And so that the meaning of the more common terms used in specifying mechanical properties may be appreciated, an explanatory appendix is included.

Acknowledgements have been offered in the appropriate places to publishers who have permitted us to reproduce material. We also wish to thank Mr. R. M. Scott and Mr. J. M. Wallbridge for photomicrographs, and the American Society for Metals for making available the following material: From Metals Handbook, Eighth Edition, Vol. 1, Figs. 4.6–4.9, 4.12, 4.13, 5.1, 6.2, 6.5, and Tables 5.1, 5.2 and 6.4. From Metals Handbook, Eighth Edition, Vol. 2, Figs. 4.5, 4.11 and Table 4.5. From *Metal Progress*, Figs. 6.6, 6.7, and Tables 6.1, 6.6 and 6.7. From Stainless Steel, by Carl Zapffe, Fig. 4.14.

February, 1966
Windsor, Ontario, Canada

J. GORDON PARR
ALBERT HANSON

Contents

Chapter 1

The Usefulness of Stainless Steels

Stainless steels do not rust in the atmosphere as most other steels do. The term "stainless" implies a resistance to staining, rusting, and pitting in the air, moist and polluted as it is, and generally defines a chromium content in excess of 11% but less than 30%. And the fact that the stuff is "steel" means that the base is iron.

Stainless steels have room-temperature yield strengths that range from 30,000 psi to more than 250,000 psi. Operating temperatures around 1400 F are common, and in some applications temperatures as high as 2000 F are reached. At the other extreme of temperature some stainless steels maintain their toughness down to temperatures approaching absolute zero.

With specific restrictions in certain types, the stainless steels can be shaped and fabricated in conventional ways. They can be produced and used in the as-cast condition; shapes can be produced by powder-metallurgy techniques; cast ingots can be rolled or forged (and this accounts for the greatest tonnage by far). The rolled product can be drawn, bent, extruded, or spun. Stainless steel can be further shaped by machining, and it can be joined by soldering, brazing, and welding. It can be used as an integral *cladding* on plain carbon or low-alloy steels.

The generic term "stainless steel" covers scores of standard compositions as well as variations bearing company trade names and special alloys made for particular applications. Stainless steels vary in their composition from a fairly simple alloy of, essentially, iron with 11% chromium, to complex alloys that include 30% chromium, substantial quantities of nickel, and half a dozen other effective elements. At the high-chromium, high-nickel end of the range they merge into other groups of heat-resisting alloys, and one has to be arbitrary about a cutoff point. If the alloy content is so high that the iron content is less than 50%, however, the alloy falls outside the stainless family. Even with these imposed restrictions on composition, the range is great, and naturally, the properties that affect fabrication and use vary enormously. It is obviously not enough to specify simply a "stainless steel."

1

Classification

The various specifying bodies categorize stainless steels according to chemical composition and other properties. For example, the American Iron and Steel Institute (AISI) lists more than 40 approved wrought stainless steel compositions; the American Society for Testing and Materials (ASTM) calls for specifications that may conform to AISI compositions but additionally require certain mechanical properties and dimensional tolerances; the Alloy Casting˜ Institute (ACI) specifies compositions for cast stainless steels within the categories of corrosion- and heat-resisting alloys; the Society of Automotive Engineers (SAE) has adopted AISI and ACI compositional specifications. In addition, federal and military specifications and manufacturers' specifications are laid down for special purposes and sometimes acquire a general acceptance.

However, all the stainless steels, whatever specifications they conform to, can be conveniently classified into five major classes that represent three distinct types of alloy constitution, or structure. These classes are ferritic, martensitic, austenitic, manganese-substituted austenitic, and precipitation-hardening. Each class is briefly described here, but will be treated in detail in Chapter 4.

Ferritic Stainless Steels. This class is so named because the crystal structure of the steel is the same as that of iron at room temperature. The alloys in the class are magnetic at room temperature and up to their Curie temperature (about 1400 F). Common alloys in the ferritic class contain between 11 and 27% chromium, no nickel, and 0.2% maximum carbon in the wrought condition. The low-chromium alloys of the class are the cheapest stainless steels, and therefore, where strength requirements can be met and the corrosion problem demands nothing more elaborate, they have an economic appeal. However, limitations to their use are associated with fabrication difficulties. Hence we find that while a production-line operation may be designed to accommodate a ferritic stainless steel (as may be the case with automotive trim), the more casual user of stainless steel seems to avoid them, even when their properties would be adequate for the application.

Martensitic Stainless Steels. Just as iron-carbon alloys are heat treatable, so alloys with a properly adjusted composition of iron, chromium and carbon (and other elements) can be quenched for maximum hardness and subsequently tempered to improve ductility. We recall that the *hardenability* of alloy steels is greater than that of plain carbon steels; that is, as the alloy content increases, so will a greater thickness be hardened under given quenching conditions. The martensitic stainless steels, which necessarily contain more than 11% chromium, have such a great hardenability that substantial thicknesses will harden during air cooling, and nothing more drastic than oil quenching is ever required. The hardness of the as-quenched martensitic stainless steel depends upon its carbon content. However, as we shall see, the development of mechanical properties through quenching and tempering is inevitably associated with increased susceptibility to corrosion.

Austenitic Stainless Steels. The high-temperature form of iron (between 1670 and 2550 F) is known as austenite. (Strictly speaking the term austenite also implies carbon in solid solution.) The structure is non-magnetic and can be retained at room temperature by appropriate alloying. The most common austenite retainer is nickel. Hence, the traditional and familiar austenitic stainless steels have a composition that contains sufficient chromium to offer corrosion resistance, together with nickel to ensure austenite at room temperature and below. The basic austenitic composition is the familiar 18% chromium, 8% nickel alloy. Both chromium and nickel contents can be increased to improve corrosion resistance, and additional elements (most commonly molybdenum) can be added to further enhance corrosion resistance.

Manganese-Substituted Austenitic Stainless Steels. The austenitic structure can be encouraged by elements other than nickel, and the substitution of manganese and nitrogen produces a class that we believe is sufficiently different in its properties to be separated from the chromium-nickel austenitic class just described. The most important difference lies in the higher strength of the manganese-substituted alloys.

Precipitation-Hardening Stainless Steels. Just as the familiar aluminum age-hardening alloys can be heat treated to improve their strength through a process that is associated with the formation of a precipitate, so stainless steels can be designed so that their composition is amenable to precipitation hardening. This class cuts across two of the other classes, to give us martensitic and austenitic precipitation-hardening stainless steels. In this class we find stainless steels with the greatest useful strength as well as the highest useful operating temperature.

Properties

Properties are substantially influenced by chemical composition. Hence specifications include chemical composition, or, more correctly, an analysis of the most important elements (traces of unreported elements also may be present).

Mechanical properties—strength, ductility, hardness, creep resistance, fatigue—of various wrought and cast stainless steels are discussed at length in Chapters 4 and 5. And the terms used are defined and discussed in Appendix A, because a fairly thorough understanding of their meanings is important. To give some idea of the ball park in which the stainless game is played, some favorable extremes of data are presented in Table 1.1.

Table 1.1. Best Performance Properties of Some Stainless Steels

Steel	Condition	Approximate composition, %	Property(a)
17–7 PH (precipitation-hardening)	Wrought, aged	17 Cr, 7 Ni, 0.05 C, 1 Mn, 1 Al	Yield strength of 260,000 psi at room temperature
301 (austenitic)	Wrought, annealed	18 Cr, 8 Ni, 0.1 C	Izod value of 100 ft-lb at −300 F
316 (austenitic)	Wrought	18 Cr, 8 Ni, 0.05 C, 2 Mo	Extremely slight rust stain on 15% of sample surface and average pit depth of 1 mil after 15-yr exposure in marine atmosphere (Kure Beach, N. C.)
HK (austenitic)	Cast	26 Cr, 20 Ni, 0.4 C	Rupture strength of 5000 psi at 1600 F after 1000 hr
HI (austenitic)	Cast	28 Cr, 15 Ni, 0.3 C	Less than 50-mil-thickness loss per year in oxidizing or reducing flue gas at 2000 F

(a) This is simply the property to which we wish to draw attention.

We assume that the reader knows how physical properties—density, thermal conductivity, electrical resistivity, and so on—are defined, to the extent that will be required by this book.

Although the corrosion-resistant properties of stainless steel are dealt with in some detail in Chapters 7 and 8, it is necessary to introduce the subject here because many applications depend so much on corrosion resistance. A stable, protective layer forms very rapidly on the surface of stainless steel when it is in most oxidizing environments, and it is produced almost immediately in air at normal temperatures. It is most simple, although not necessarily correct, to assume that this layer is a thin, transparent film of chromic oxide.

If corrosive mediums attack the oxide, or establish conditions that prevent its renewal when it is abraded, then the steel will succumb to corrosion. Under these circumstances, corrosion can be mitigated to some extent by the influence of other alloying elements that, in any case, play their part in specific environments. But in the broad case, and considering the simple model of stainless steel protected by a chromic oxide film, we would anticipate attack by the reducing mineral acids (hydrochloric, hydrofluoric) and by reducing organic acids. Depending upon oxygen content, concentration, temperature, and other factors, sulfuric acid is or is not corrosive. Nitric acid, a highly oxidizing liquid, maintains the protective oxide layer. In the organic acids associated with most food products (citric, malic, tartaric) stainless steel resists corrosion; hence its wide application in the foodstuffs and dairy industries.

The outstanding performance of the stainless steels is in atmospheric environments. In dry or wet rural atmospheres any stainless is—to put it crassly—stainless. In polluted atmospheres the performance varies very considerably from one grade of stainless to another.

Selection

A recent survey conducted by the magazine *Metal Progress* showed that the major reason for the selection of stainless steel by 7600 respondents was corrosion resistance and heat resistance. Other reasons offered included strength, cryogenic properties, weldability, formability, machinability, and cost advantage. Equally important, 76% of the respondents indicated that they plan to use increasing amounts of stainless during the next five years. Tables 1.2 and 1.3 give some production figures for various types and products of stainless steel.

The choice of a material is not simply based on a single requirement, however, even though a specific condition (for example, corrosion service)

Table 1.2. Production of Stainless and Heat-Resisting Steels in the United States(a)

	Ingot production, thousands of tons					Total mill shipments(e), thousands of tons
Year	Total(b)	Chromium(c)	Chromium-nickel	Manganese-substituted	Heat-resisting(d)	
1957	1044	378	604	26	36	620
1958	893	314	528	30	21	493
1959	1129	391	688	28	21	615
1960	1001	337	623	22	19	579
1961	1136	362	712	32	30	565
1962	1084	356	661	39	28	632
1963	1202	362	764	50	27	659
1964	1440	...	...	...	...	771

(a) Data were taken from various sources, but most are from the American Iron and Steel Institute.
(b) Includes stainless and heat-resisting steels
(c) Includes ferritic and martensitic grades
(d) Includes stainless and higher-alloy steels
(e) It is difficult to relate ingot production and mill shipments, because ingots may be exported and, equally, a mill may produce from imported ingots. However, the yield of mill products from mill ingots is about 55%.

Table 1.3. Mill Shipments of Stainless Steel,
Excluding Semifinished Products, in 1964
in the United States(a)

Product	Mill shipments, net tons
Cold rolled strip	254,780
Cold rolled sheet	172,189
Cold finished bars	70,548
Hot rolled bars (and light shapes)	45,749
Hot rolled sheet	37,982
Pressure tubing	26,873
Wire	24,914
Hot rolled strip	23,556

(a) Data from the American Iron and Steel Institute.

may narrow the range of possibilities. For instance, in the choice of stainless steel for railroad cars, while corrosion resistance is one determining factor, strength is particularly significant. The higher price of stainless steel compared with plain carbon steel is moderated by the fact that the stainless has about twice the allowable design strength. This not only cuts the amount of steel purchased, but, by reducing the dead weight of the vehicle, raises the load that can be hauled. The same sort of reasoning is even more critical in aircraft and space vehicles.

But weight saving alone may be accomplished by other materials, for example, the high-strength low-alloy steels in rolling stock and titanium alloys in aircraft. Thus, the selection of a material involves a careful appraisal of all service requirements as well as a consideration of the ways in which the required parts can be made. It would be foolish to select a material on the basis of its predicted performance if the required shape could be produced only with such difficulty that cost skyrocketed.

The applicability of stainless steels may be limited by some specific factor, for example, an embrittlement problem or susceptibility to a particular corrosive environment. In general terms, the obvious limitations are:

1. In chloride environments susceptibility to pitting or stress-corrosion cracking requires careful appraisal. One cannot blindly assume that a stainless steel of some sort will do. In fact, it is possible that no stainless will serve.

2. The temperature of satisfactory operation depends upon the load to be supported, the time of its application, and the atmosphere. However, to offer a round number for the sake of marking a limit, we suggest a maximum temperature of 1600 F. Common stainless steels can be used for short times above this temperature, or for extended periods if the load

is only a few thousand pounds per square inch. But if the loads or the operating periods are great, then more exotic alloys are called for.

The type of compilation given previously in Table 1.1 ignores that prime engineering parameter, cost. And while it indicates upper performance limits, it does not suggest any guide to economy. For example, while 316 performs well in the Kure Beach atmosphere, the use of this comparatively high-priced stainless steel is not required for architectural purposes. And the very high yield strength of the 17% chromium, 7% nickel precipitation-hardening steel would not be called for in, let us say, rolling-stock construction. The data in Table 1.4 suggest, in a very broad way, the most economical class of stainless for various types of service. (Here we assume that general considerations of corrosion resistance, strength, and high-temperature properties call for the use of a stainless steel.) The choice may be completely changed, however, through considerations of fabrication or availability.

In some applications, the use of a stainless-clad material offers an economically attractive combination of a corrosion-resistant surface bonded on to a suitably strong, and reasonably cheap, backing. Clad plate, sheet, and tubular products have been available for over 20 years, and current annual production in the United States is estimated to be greater than 250,000 tons. Any of a number of techniques produce a stainless steel layer integrally bonded to a plain carbon or low-alloy steel

Table 1.4. The Most Economical Class of Stainless for Various Types of Service(a)

Type of service	Stainless class
Atmospheric corrosion	Austenitic and manganese-substituted austenitic
Interior trim	Ferritic
Fresh-water corrosion	Ferritic
Marine environment	Austenitic and manganese-substituted austenitic(b)
Low temperatures	Austenitic and manganese-substituted austenitic
High temperatures up to 1200 F	Ferritic
High temperatures above 1200 F	Austenitic or precipitation-hardening
High strength at normal temperatures	Martensitic
High strength at elevated temperatures	Precipitation-hardening
High strength at low temperatures	Austenitic or manganese-substituted austenitic

(a) It is assumed here that general considerations of corrosion resistance, strength, and high-temperature properties seem to indicate the use of a stainless steel.

(b) As conditions become more severe, higher alloy contents are required.

backing, and the thickness of the stainless cladding is usually between 10 and 20% of the total plate thickness. It is important to point out that an economic analysis of comparative prices of solid stainless or clad material must include the cost of fabricating the material into the structure. The difficulties that may arise, for example, in welding the composite material, can be overcome, but probably add to fabricating costs.

Applications Involving Resistance to Atmospheric Corrosion

Buildings. The austenitic stainless steels are being used in increasing amounts in buildings—not for concealed structural members, but for facings. Once limited to trim, stainless is now used for entire exposed areas. Early buildings using austenitic stainless are the Chrysler building and the Empire State building. More recently, the IBM office building in Pittsburgh's Golden Triangle, Union Carbide's 52-story headquarters, and the Inland Steel Company's skyscraper have utilized the manganese-substituted stainless steels. Stainless, in addition to its corrosion resistance, is architecturally and structurally compatible with most other building materials. Higher strengths and improved designs are reducing the installed costs, and maintenance costs are low.

Rolling Stock, Autos, and Trucks. The use of ferritic stainless steel in automotive trim was largely responsible for the ¼-million-ton annual production of 430. Alternates, including the manganese-substituted austenitic grades, are now being used to a greater extent, and the possibilities of lighter-gage material with adequate strength and resistance to denting offer prospects for greater stainless applications.

Ferritic stainless steels, with minimal chromium contents of about 11% and very low carbon levels to offset the cheese-pared chromium, have recently been introduced for automotive mufflers and tail pipes. This material is readily welded, and in muffler production high-frequency resistance welding offers the best production-line method.

There is an increasing use of the manganese-substituted austenitic material in trailers, subway cars, and commuter cars. Six hundred subway cars recently ordered by the New York City Transit Authority are based on a cost-saving of almost eight million dollars, which reflects a saving in capital cost of two million dollars, a saving in maintenance cost of ½-million dollars over 35 years, and most significant, a saving in power consumption, through lighter weight of the cars, of 5½ million dollars over 35 years.

Compared with other high-strength materials that compete with conventional plain carbon structural grades, stainless has the advantages of corrosion resistance (hence no painting) and faster welding processes.

The use of stainless in railway rolling stock is swelled by the advantages of a corrosion-resistant "slideable" material for hopper cars, and when "containerization" (thankfully this is not *our* word) becomes more widely accepted, stainless containers will probably be used.

Furniture. Probably the mildest form of corrosive attack is found in offices and homes. Yet stainless is increasingly used on account of its appearance (which, in turn, is due to its resistance to tarnishing and rusting) and the fact that the absence of a paint coat eliminates the problems of chipping, peeling, and deterioration.

The expanding application of stainless is due to more economical methods of making tubing and shaped hollow sections and to the development of furniture designs that match the properties of the stainless.

Power Generation. Power generation involves water and steam as corrodents. Stainless blading in steam turbines is common, but a more recent application is austenitic stainless tubing in heat exchangers and condensers. The disadvantage of stainless compared with other accepted materials, for example, copper alloys, plain carbon and low-alloy steels, appears to be its poor thermal conductivity. However, while this is undeniable, heat transfer through the other materials can become reduced through the buildup of scale and other corrosion products, and after a period of operation, stainless, which remains clean, may offer better heat-transfer properties.

The dangers of chloride attack can be reduced by specifying the more highly alloyed austenitic grades. This subject is dealt with in Chapter 8.

Laundry Equipment. Corrosion resistance, ease of fabrication, and strength, favor the use of austenitic stainless steels.

Applications Involving Resistance to Other Corrodents

Food-Processing and Kitchen Equipment. Many varieties of stainless are used in food preparation and serving. Indeed, their use may be demanded by legislation. Applications range from the familiar domestic kitchenware and tableware, to tank trucks, pasteurizing vessels, and bakery plants. The gleam of stainless steel is to be seen throughout dairies, confectionery plants and food-packing plants.

Agriculture. While the use of stainless has long been accepted in the food-processing business, it is now becoming more familiar around the farm. The trend toward fertilizers and sprays introduces difficult corrosion problems in equipment, and a frequent answer is to be found in the austenitic stainless steels. Although initial cost is higher, a 20-year life is generally predicted, with little maintenance.

Textiles. To maintain true colors in fabrics, processing machinery must be easily cleaned to facilitate dye changes and must remain clean during use. Any contamination of dyes or bleaching solutions not only results in a loss of chemicals, but can ruin the textile product. The austenitic stainless steels are used in textile machines and in vessels that carry peroxide and chlorine bleaches in dying plants.

Hospital and Surgical Equipment. Martensitic stainless steels are the accepted materials for surgical instruments: they retain a sharpened edge, are easily sterilized, and resist corrosion. Sterilizing equipment, autoclaves, instrument cabinets, and operating tables are usually made of austenitic stainless steel. Kitchens, examination rooms, and laboratories specify stainless installations.

Chemical and Petrochemical Plants. Here are some of the toughest corrosion problems, many of them involving elevated temperatures and vigorous corrodents. In the hydrocracking of petroluem distillates, hydrogen sulphide corrosion is combated by austenitic stainless steels. The increasing operating temperature of catalytic cracking units (up to 1300 F) has led to a greater use of stainless, which is replacing lower-alloy and plain carbon steels.

The chemical industry considers austenitic stainless steel as a standard material of construction: in the production of acids, ammonia, fertilizer, and plastics a compromise often has to be sought between the high strength of some of the newer alloys and their somewhat reduced corrosion resistance.

Applications Involving High Strength at Elevated Temperature

A number of the groups already itemized fall into this category, for example, steam turbines and chemical and petrochemical equipment. However, the call for high-temperature strength as a prime requirement is nowhere more insistent than in aircraft and space-vehicles.

Aircraft designers seek a high strength-weight ratio at temperatures up to 600 F for materials to be used in aircraft skins. Eighty-five per cent of the skin of the B70—and of other supersonic planes—must be made of heat-resistant material. In the B70, honeycomb panels for wing surfaces and fuselage are made of precipitation-hardening semi-austenitic stainless steel. These alloys are finding many applications in contemporary aircraft: in engine pods, nozzles, and structural parts.

In space vehicles, the precipitation-hardening alloys are used in rocket cases, while austenitic grades are chosen for propellant tanks. The Atlas and Centaur were substantially constructed from austenitic stainless, and the 35-in.-diameter shell of the Explorer XVII is made of stainless.

An economic choice of stainless steel must be based upon a knowledge of the properties of the material as well as a general appreciation of the response of the various classes to common fabrication processes. The subsequent chapters of this book deal with these topics. However, a very brief note about the historical development of the stainless steels is given in Chapter 2, and for readers who need to brush up their physical metallurgy, Chapter 3 is offered.

Chapter 2
A Brief History

Stainless steels form part of the great section cut through history by the development of iron alloys, beginning about 1400 B.C. with the first man-made iron. The so-called industrial revolution was made possible only through Cort's improvement in ironmaking methods and his introduction of mills to produce rolled sections. Then, a little more than a hundred years ago Henry Bessemer invented the pneumatic process that led the way to mass-produced steel, which is now made in open hearths, oxygen-blown vessels, Bessemers, and electric furnaces at the world rate of one million tons each day.

With the mass production of steel came a scientific interest in the material. Of course, there were brilliant examples of earlier research. But it was not until about 1890 that the constitution and properties of steels were methodically investigated. By 1920 metallurgists were applying methods of x-ray diffraction to the study of metallic properties and so supplemented the microscopical techniques made possible by Sorby in the mid-nineteenth century.

Stainless steels enter the picture at the turn of the century. Earlier work was related to the properties of ferrochromium, and, indeed, Berthier produced an iron—1% chromium alloy and remarked upon its corrosion resistance. Carl Zapffe, in his book "Stainless Steels" (ASM 1949), pointed out the number of experiments that just missed discovering stainless steel: alloys either very high or very low in chromium were tested, and they usually contained a high carbon content. Perhaps the most remarkable near miss was that of Hadfield who, in 1892, produced steels containing as much as 17% chromium, but with carbon contents in excess of 1%. Hadfield assessed the corrosion resistance of his new materials by testing them in 50% sulfuric acid, to which stainless steel is not resistant, and concluded that chromium impaired the corrosion resistance.

The period 1900 to 1915 is rich in metallurgical discovery: the puzzling allotropy of iron became resolved; the effects of carbon on the properties of iron were systematized; principles accepted by the pure scientist were applied to metal systems; the mechanisms of transformations were investigated by microscope, thermocouple, dilatometer, and x-rays. And it is within this period that we must place, despite the earlier work that came so close to discovery, the beginning of the stainless steels.

In France and England the principal types of stainless steel were derived, and in Germany Monnartz discovered many of the principles of the corrosion resistance of stainless steel—the critical chromium content, the role of carbon, passivity, the effect of molybdenum. Simultaneously, both in Europe and in the United States, the industrial importance of the stainless steels was recognized: patents were applied for and granted; litigations followed. Zapffe, whose researches in this subject place him in a pre-eminent position to offer a judgment, suggests that while the pioneers of stainless steel are often credited with discovery, the true discoverers were Guillet, who was responsible for the fundamental metallurgy of the stainless steels, Monnartz, who discovered their corrosion resistance, Giesen and Portevin, who complemented the work of Guillet, and Brearley and Maurer, who determined the industrial value of the alloys.

Work over the past 20 years has been more specific, and we do not find such sweeping and grand discoveries as the earlier investigators gave us. Nor is this surprising: the wheel can only be invented once, and subsequent technologists seem by contrast to have contributed only rather minor spokes. However, within the wealth of work that has contributed to our knowledge of the corrosion behavior, weldability, strength and general applicability of the stainless steels, two discoveries seem to be of great significance.

The first is the substitution of manganese for nickel in the chromium-nickel stainless steels—the austenitic group. Because of shortages of nickel during World War II these alloys were developed in Europe and have since become standard grades. Manganese is not nearly as strong in its effect as nickel is, and at common chromium contents it is not possible to form an austenitic stainless steel with chromium and manganese alone. For this reason, nickel is also present, to the extent of about 5%. However, nitrogen is powerful in its austenitizing effect; therefore, in the stainless steels in which manganese substitutes for some of the nickel, we expect an unusually high nitrogen content, too. The specifications call for a maximum nitrogen content in these grades of 0.25%.

The second major development in recent years is the precipitation-hardening stainless steels. Although papers describing the characteristics of such steels appeared about 1930, precipitation-hardening stainlesses have come into common use only during the last ten years or so.

The principle of precipitation hardening is dealt with in Chapter 3. For the purposes of introduction here, it is sufficient to say that strength of precipitation-hardening alloys is developed by the collection of clusters of atoms in the base-metal matrix. The clusters form during special heat treatments and eventually become definable precipitates of compounds, but at the stage where the precipitate can be defined, the strength of the alloy usually begins to fall. As a result, the heat treatment is designed to allow the development of preprecipitates. The choice of alloying elements for precipitation-hardening effects is usually made empirically; however, we would expect the addition to be one that did not, for example, form weak grain-boundary networks at operating temperature or reduce the corrosion resistance too greatly. Common additions include aluminum or copper and columbium.

Chapter 3

Some Metallurgical Principles and Heat Treatment Processes

The mechanical properties and thus the fabrication and use of a metal or alloy depend on its constitution, that is, its internal structure. And its internal structure, in turn, depends not only on its composition but also on previous deformation and heat treatment. This chapter attempts to outline some of the aspects of metallic structure and heat treatment processes that are pertinent to our discussion of stainless steels.

Structure of Metals

Solid metals are crystalline; that is, their atoms are (so far as we need be concerned) regularly arranged. Among the many arrangements of atoms that occur in metals, we need describe only two. The first of these is called the body-centered cubic structure and is illustrated in Fig. 3.1, which shows a unit of the pattern of a body-centered cubic metal. The second is the face-centered cubic structure, of which a unit of pattern is shown in Fig. 3.2. We remember that the diameter of an atom of iron is about

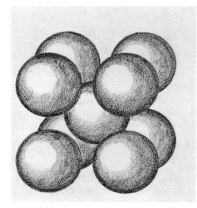 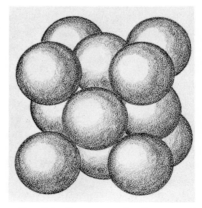

Fig. 3.1. Body-centered cubic unit of structure   *Fig. 3.2. Face-centered cubic unit of structure*

15

2.5 × 10^{-8} cm. Thus the smallest piece of iron that we can see contains billions more atoms than there are people in the world. This very large number of atoms, which evens out statistical fluctuations, makes the behavior of metal solids of reasonable size predictable.

In a single crystal of iron at temperatures below 1670 F the atoms of iron are arranged in the body-centered cubic configuration. This structure is known as alpha iron. Between 1670 and 2550 F, the iron atoms are in the face-centered cubic configuration, known as gamma iron. Between 2550 and the melting temperature (2800 F) the iron reverts to its body-centered arrangement—but we can avoid discussing this.

However, while this reasonably describes the two structures of pure iron crystals, we have to take into account two complicating factors. First, a chunk of metal usually consists of many crystals. Under the microscope these can be readily delineated. The structure of a piece of reasonably pure iron is shown in Fig. 3.3. The separate crystals are all composed of (essentially) iron atoms, and their only difference is that their orientations

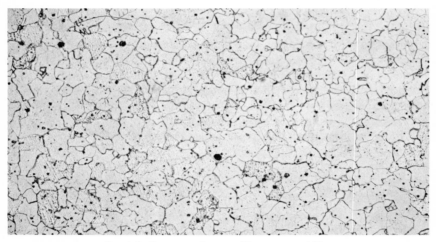

Fig. 3.3. Structure of reasonably pure iron. 100×

are different (Fig. 3.4). This difference in orientations leads to what are called crystal boundaries or, more commonly, grain boundaries, between the crystals, in whose locations the atomic arrangement is rather badly disarranged (Fig. 3.5). In a two-dimensional view, the grain boundary appears as a line but, of course, in the three-dimensional solid piece of metal, grain boundaries are surfaces between crystals. And the disarray of atoms at these surfaces is associated with a pronounced reactivity. We will discuss, in later chapter, an effect known as *sensitization*, in which

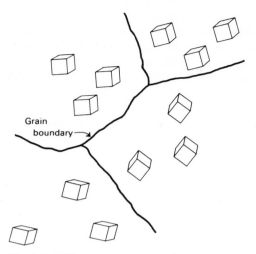

Fig. 3.4. *Different orientations in adjacent grains*

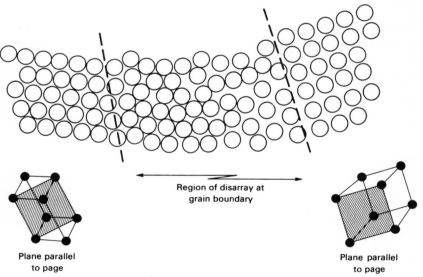

Region of disarray at
grain boundary

Plane parallel
to page

Plane parallel
to page

Fig. 3.5. *Atomic disarray at grain boundary*

chromium carbides form at the grain boundaries in stainless steels. This phenomenon illustrates the point that reactions within metallic solids tend to take place at the grain-boundary regions.

A second complicating factor arises because metals of greatest commercial importance are rarely pure elements. We already know, for example, that stainless steel is an alloy of iron with chromium, at least. Other elements are present, too. Now, an alloy of iron with 13 wt % of chromium will consist of a random mixture of iron and chromium atoms. The chromium atoms are approximately the same size as the iron atoms, and about one in seven atoms in the alloy will be a chromium atom. This mixture of atoms in a crystal, in which the atoms of the second element are simply distributed in the parent crystal structure, is known as a *solid solution*. In the example we have described, because the chromium atoms are to be found in exactly similar sites to the iron atoms, the solid solution is known as *substitutional*.

If we added carbon atoms to the alloy of iron and chromium, these would distribute themselves in the gaps between the other atoms, so long as we were content to add only about 0.1%.* The carbon is said to have formed an *interstitial solid solution.* However, if larger amounts of carbon are added, the structure will not accept the carbon atoms in solution— in much the same way as we can only dissolve a limited amount of salt in water at a given temperature. The carbon atoms that are in excess of the solubility limit combine with the chromium atoms to form chromium carbide.

Under the microscope a solid solution cannot be distinguished from a pure element (except occasionally by a color change). Figure 3.6 is a micrograph of an austenitic stainless steel—a solid solution of chromium and nickel in iron. Compare this with Fig. 3.3. However, if the solid

Fig. 3.6. Micrograph of an austenitic stainless steel. 200×

*Where not otherwise indicated, percentage compositions, additions or substitutions are given in weight per cent.

solubility for a particular element is exceeded, a second *phase* forms, as we have just mentioned in the case of chromium carbide formation. The molecules of chromium carbide tend to segregate at the grain boundaries and, if they form sufficiently large volumes, they can be seen under the microscope.

With this in mind, we can begin to appreciate the structures of the ferritic and austenitic classes of stainless steels. The ferritic class has the body-centered cubic structure of alpha iron, and depending on its composition, it has between one in eight and one in three iron atoms substituted by chromium atoms. The structure will also contain a small number of atoms of manganese and other elements, substituting for some of the iron atoms. Carbon is also present: some of the carbon atoms take up interstitial positions; others form carbides, which may be present at the grain boundaries or (depending upon the history of the alloy) distributed within the grains.

In the austenitic class the effect of the nickel addition is to stabilize the face-centered structure (which in pure iron forms between 1670 and 2550 F) at room temperature. In the common alloy with about 18% chromium and 8% nickel, we would expect to find the atomic arrangement shown in Fig. 3.2, but with about one in five of the atoms being chromium and about one in thirteen being nickel—a substitutional solid solution of chromium and nickel in iron. Again, atoms of other elements are also present; carbon is distributed in the interatomic spaces, but may also form carbides, depending upon the prior history of the alloy.

Strengthening Mechanisms

There are many effects of alloy additions: chromium, as we have already pointed out, imparts properties of corrosion resistance. And we would find a change in all the physical, mechanical, and chemical properties as chromium is added to iron. Among other things, the strength of the iron is increased by alloy additions. However, strengthening by substitutional elements is not usually very effective.

There are three pertinent methods of strengthening stainless steel: (*a*) work hardening, (*b*) martensitic hardening, and (*c*) precipitation hardening.

Work Hardening. If a metal or alloy is plastically deformed by bending, squeezing, hammering, or any means that takes it beyond its yield point, it becomes harder and stronger. Its ductility, by the way, is simultaneously reduced. This effect, work hardening, is accompanied by a distortion of the crystals, and under the microscope the worked structure has the appearance of Fig. 3.7. The original properties of the metal can be

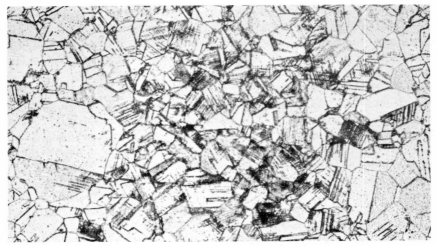

Fig. 3.7. Distortion of crystals produced by working. 200×

restored by heating the piece above the *recrystallization temperature.* Some metals—pure lead is a common one—have a recrystallization temperature that is around room temperature; hence they will not work harden at room temperature. The recrystallization temperature depends most markedly upon the purity of the metal, and the effect of alloy additions is to increase the recrystallization temperature. Pure iron may recrystallize at as low as 300 F; austenitic stainless steel begins to recrystallize at about 1000 F.

Different alloys respond to cold working to different extents. Sometimes a substantial increase in strength is associated with a change of crystal structure. For example, when some of the austenitic stainless steels are cold worked, the face-centered cubic arrangement of atoms tends to change to the body-centered structure. This, for reasons that we will not attempt to discuss, causes a pronounced hardness and strength increase.

If a metal is worked above its recrystallization temperature, it is said to be *hot worked*, and we may imagine a simultaneous process of deformation and recrystallization occurring.

Martensitic Hardening. The phenomenon of hardening when a piece of steel is heated and plunged into water is familiar to all of us. The hardening is associated with a change of crystal structure from face-centered to body-centered cubic but the active atom in bringing about the hardness increase is carbon. In very crude terms, we can rationalize the phenomenon in the following way: in austenite, the carbon atom is fairly comfortably disposed—the face-centered cubic arrangement of iron (with or without substituted chromium) can take up to about 2 wt % of carbon in its interstitial positions. However, when the alloy is cooled and the iron atoms take up their body-centered cubic arrangement, the carbon atoms are no longer so easily accommodated, because (at its simplest) the gaps between the iron atoms are no longer big enough to accommodate the carbon atom. On slow cooling, the carbon tags on to the atoms around it, forms carbides, and precipitates where it can. However, if cooling is very rapid, there is no time for the carbon atoms to move around to form precipitated carbides: they are trapped in the newly formed body-centered cubic structure in which, as we have just mentioned, they are not readily accommodated. Hence this structure is badly distorted through the presence of the carbon atoms and its distortion brings about an increase in hardness and strength.

The rapidly cooled structure is known as *martensite*. The cooling rate required to produce such a structure depends upon the composition of the alloy: in general terms, the more alloy present the slower is the required cooling rate to produce martensite. At stainless steel compositions (which will be more completely discussed in the next chapter) air cooling is often sufficient to produce the hard, martensitic structure. However, the actual hardness attained depends entirely upon the amount of carbon in the steel: the more carbon the harder, stronger, but less ductile will be the product.

The martensitic material usually has inadequate ductility, particularly if its carbon content is much above 0.2%. To improve the ductility (and simultaneously reduce the strength) the steel is *tempered*: it is heated so that the martensite begins to decompose, when some of the carbon atoms have the opportunity of forming carbides, hence relieving the structural distortion.

Precipitation Hardening. The phenomenon of precipitation hardening is most familiar in aluminum alloys. The general principle is to produce a supercooled solid solution from which, on *aging*, compounds precipitate. Just as it is possible to supercool a liquid solution of salt in water, by cooling it rapidly (and carefully), so it is possible to produce a super-cooled solid solution. Hence, at room temperature we have a solid solution that is not stable, but *metastable*: there are more alloying element atoms in solution than the structure can really put up with. Given the chance, the structure will induce these atoms to form a separate phase. The chance is offered by time and it may be made more attractive by heat.

During the early stages of the precipitation process, the unwelcome atoms move out of their ungenerous quarters and begin to combine with other atoms about them. Eventually they will form precipitates that are visible under the microscope, but it is during the early stages (before we can readily see what is going on) that the greatest strength increase occurs —during what is called the *preprecipitation* stage. When visible precipitates have formed, the strength is usually on the decline, and the alloy is said to have *overaged*.

The precipitates associated with the hardening process are complex and we will not attempt to review the literature that describes their identification. It is, however, easier to state that in the precipitation-hardening stainless steels, additional elements (aluminum, molybdenum, copper) that are active in the precipitation-hardening process are introduced, and heat treatments are devised to produce first the supersaturated solid solution and then the preprecipitation stage.

Solid-state transformation processes such as precipitation-hardening phenomena are very complex. The reader who wishes to study the subject further will find many texts on the subject. Our purpose is simply to offer an introduction to Chapter 4.

Heat Treatment Processes

Annealing. The purpose of annealing is to put a material in its soft condition. We hope that it will not be confused with tempering, which, as we described above, is an integral second part of the double treatment of quenching and tempering and is used to obtain a desirable combination of strength and ductility in hardenable steels.

Obviously, annealing means different processes to different materials. For example, the martensitic stainless steels can be annealed by heating them above their critical temperature (into the austenite range) and cooling them so slowly that ferrite rather than martensite forms. Or they can be annealed by heating them to a subcritical temperature, at which the martensite formed during a prior cooling will decompose. The purpose here is not to obtain a satisfactory combination of strength and ductility (which we seek in quenching and tempering) but simply to soften. The high-temperature anneal induces the more complete softening and it is known as a *full* anneal.

There is no distinctive *full* or *subcritical* anneal for the austenitic and ferritic stainless steels. Further, because the austenitic grades do not harden by martensitic transformation, annealing removes hardness that has been developed solely by cold working. It also can be used to redissolve carbides precipitated at grain boundaries of austenitic stainless steels during sensitization, which, as we will see in Chapter 4, occurs when the steel is heated at temperatures between 800 and 1500 F and results in decreased corrosion resistance.

Stress Relieving. While the heat treatment known as stress-relieving may in fact involve annealing, the intention of the process is not to soften the steel (although that may, of course, occur) but to reduce residual stresses built into the structure during shaping and welding.

Homogenization. The additional heat treatment of *homogenization*, in which segregation is leveled out, generally involves heating at about 2000 F, and this is particularly desirable in the precipitation-hardening alloys. Austenitic castings are rapidly cooled from their homogenizing temperature.

Nitriding. Thin, but very hard, surfaces with excellent wear resistance and improved fatigue properties can be obtained by nitriding. In principle, the process consists of subjecting the steel part to an active nitrogenous source — usually ammonia — at about 1000 F. No subsequent quenching is required.

Response to nitriding depends upon alloy composition. Largely because of their chromium content, the stainless steels can be nitrided (the austenitic grades with most difficulty), and a layer between 0.004 and 0.008 in. thick develops during a 48-hr treatment. (After this time, little further thickening occurs.)

Prior to nitriding, the part must be stress relieved, and the nitriding process must be the last heat treatment performed. A little growth occurs as a result of the formation of the nitrided layer, and experiments are necessary to determine the precise shape change to be expected under given conditions.

The surface of the stainless must be *depassivated* by a reduction process or some other suitable means of removing oxide, and absolute cleanliness is essential.

Nitrided stainless steel parts have been successfully used in valve stems, shafts, bushings, and fiber guides. Corrosion resistance is reduced, and response to corrosive environments should be evaluated by tests.

Practical Aspects. Heat treatment requirements begin with thorough cleaning of the articles. Traces of organic materials, finger prints, pencil marks, must be completely removed, and furnace fixtures must be of clean materials that will not contaminate the stainless — they are generally made of stainless or of heat-resisting nickel alloy.

The heating process can be conducted in a furnace, salt bath, induction coil, or open flame. The last is usually restricted to torch heating as part of a field welding cycle. Induction annealing also is applicable to heat treatment of welds, and it is particularly adaptable to in-line heat treatment of a continuous product or a succession of individual items. However, furnaces and salt baths are more common.

Furnaces. Heating can be by burners or electrical resistance. Furnaces heated by burners can be open or muffle. Stainless is commonly heated in an air atmosphere, and the scale is subsequently removed by pickling. The amount of scaling can be minimized in open-fired furnaces by controlling the air-fuel ratio, and the danger of carburization is avoided by maintaining sufficient free oxygen in the atmosphere.

Externally generated atmospheres of the endothermic-base class are not usually satisfactory because of their tendency to carburize. Further, their hydrogen content can lead to embrittlement of the martensitic grades. Exothermic-base gases are satisfactory, but will cause some scaling.

For complete inertness, argon or helium can be used but the cost can rarely be justified. Hence, in bright annealing, dissociated ammonia is common. So that nitriding is avoided, the ammonia must be dissociated at a high temperature; 1800 F represents a fair compromise between completeness of decomposition at economic rates, and deterioration of equipment.

The gas used in bright annealing must be dry. Dew points not exceeding -80 to -100 F are recommended.

Temperature control—necessary in all heat treatment processes—is particularly important in stainless steel heat treatment, because satisfactory temperature ranges are often narrowed by efforts to avoid embrittling or sensitizing.

Hydrogen embrittlement may occur in the martensitic grades as a result of hydrogen pickup in the furnace (as, indeed, it may arise during pickling and other chemical treatments). The effect does not usually arise if the cooling rate is fairly slow, and it can be removed by tempering.

Salt Baths. The heat treatment of martensitic stainless steels can be carried out conveniently by heating the part in molten salt. Advice on suitable salts, containers, and heating methods is best obtained from suppliers. The salts commonly used are either sodium carbonate or barium chloride (probably with additions of other chlorides). The salt bath should be used exclusively for stainless so that contamination problems are minimized.

Soaking times are best determined by experiment. The removed article should be thoroughly cleaned of salt as soon as possible.

Salt baths can, of course, be used for annealing processes: the decision to use salt or furnace is an economic one.

Chapter 4

Mechanical Properties of Wrought
Stainless Steels

This chapter describes the pertinent mechanical properties* of the principal wrought stainless steels and relates these properties to their constitution — so far as is necessary. Chapter 1 introduced the five classes of stainless steels. Because this classification is derived from constitutional characteristics, which, in turn, are responsible for the properties and uses of the stainless steels, we will follow it here. This chapter will first skirmish with the rationale behind the classification. Then it will describe the general properties of stainless steels in each group and discuss the principal members of each group.

The development of mechanical properties in steels by martensitic strengthening was introduced in Chapter 3. If the steel contains sufficient chromium that it is stainless, undergoes a martensitic transformation on cooling, and contains sufficient carbon to harden it, then a heat treatable stainless steel is the result. With such a large chromium content we would expect the steel to have a high hardenability; that is, it will harden even at slow cooling rates. Indeed, this class of stainless steel is generally air hardening.

But a complication arises. The amount of chromium that can be added is limited. As pointed out in Chapter 3, iron changes from the body-centered cubic alpha phase (ferrite) to the face-centered cubic gamma phase (austenite) at 1670 F (known as the A_3 temperature) and back to the body-centered cubic alpha phase at 2550 F (the A_4 temperature). However, the addition of chromium reduces the range over which the face-centered cubic phase is stable; the A_4 temperature drops very rapidly, and the A_3 temperature, after an initial lowering, rises to meet the A_4 temperature. At about 13% chromium, the face-centered cubic structure does not occur. This is summarized in Fig. 4.1. Hence we speak of the effect of chromium as producing a *gamma loop*: there is a restricted area of compositions and temperatures (the area of the loop) in which the face-centered cubic structure is stable. An alloy of iron and chromium must lie in this area if it is to be heat treatable by quenching and tempering. From

*Tabulated *physical* properties data are given in Appendix B.

25

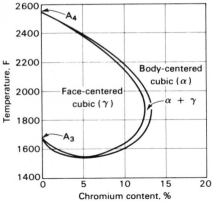

Fig. 4.1. Partial iron-chromium phase
diagram

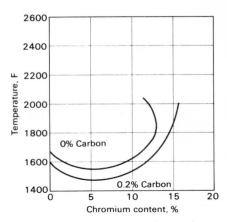

Fig. 4.2. Effect of 0.2% carbon on the
gamma loop

Fig. 4.1 we see that if the chromium content exceeds about 12%, no austenitic structure can be produced at any temperature: the possibilities of quenching to produce martensite are removed.

At 12% Cr a stainless steel is only just stainless: there is barely enough chromium present to ensure passivity. Fortunately, however, the effect of adding carbon to the iron-chromium alloy is to spread the gamma loop. Figure 4.2 shows the location of the loop for iron-chromium alloys containing 0.2% carbon. Thus it is possible to produce an alloy composition that is hardenable by quenching and, at the same time, contains sufficient carbon to offer reasonable hardness and strength. Had the effect of carbon been the other way, that is, if carbon were to *restrict* the gamma loop, then we would have no martensitic stainless steels.

The point should be made that there is nothing magical about these diagrams. They are simply a means of indicating what phases are present at various compositions and temperatures: they are determined by laborious experiment and are redetermined annually by subdued students in North American universities.

Now, if the chromium content (for any given carbon level) exceeds the limits of the gamma loop, the alloy will, at all temperatures to its melting point, be body-centered cubic. The structure—the way the atoms are arranged—is the same as that in pure iron at room temperature. Such an alloy is therefore known as ferritic: it cannot be made to go through a martensitic transformation, because it cannot change its structure. In the ferritic stainless steels, the amount of chromium that can be added is not limited. We are not caught in the same sort of box that restricts the chemistry of the martensitic stainless steels, but we will see (when the ferritic steels are discussed) that constitutional complications of another sort arise.

The third class of stainless steels is derived by stabilizing austenite at room temperature. Figure 4.1 showed the effect of chromium in forming a gamma loop. The effect of nickel on iron is to open up the range of stability of austenite. The austenite region in an alloy of iron with 18% chromium and varying amounts of nickel is shown in Fig. 4.3. However, while this diagram implies that at low temperatures even alloys containing quite high nickel contents will transform to ferrite, the transformation is so sluggish that austenite persists on cooling the alloy from the austenite region to room temperature (and usually to subzero temperatures). Figure 4.4 shows the compositions of iron-chromium-nickel alloys (zero carbon) for which austenite is persistent at room temperature.

For most applications the corrosion resistance of an austenitic stainless steel containing about 16% chromium is not very much changed as its nickel content is reduced from 8 to 4%. Hence elements other than nickel can be used to fulfill the requirement of producing austenite at room temperature, without adversely affecting corrosion resistance. The manganese-substituted austenitic stainless steels have a nickel content reduced to between 3.5 and 6.0%. Austenitizing is effected by the addition of 5 to 10% manganese, and nitrogen in amounts not exceeding 0.25%.

While the original introduction of these steels on the market was to offset a nickel shortage, they should no longer be regarded as a substitute. As we will see when the group is discussed, they have a greater strength than the simple austenitic class. Hence, even though they have little price

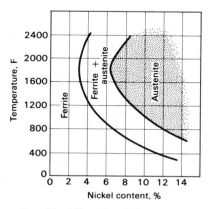

Fig. 4.3. Effect of nickel content on the stability of austenite in an iron alloy containing 18% chromium

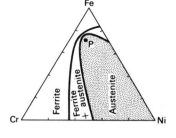

Fig. 4.4. Compositions of iron-chromium-nickel alloys for which austenite persists at room temperature. Point P indicates the position of an alloy containing 18% chromium and 8% nickel

advantage on a per-ton basis, they should offer a saving in that the required section to support a given load is reduced.

Before proceeding, it would be well to point out a difficulty associated with the classification of stainless steels. For example, the region above the nose of the curve in Fig. 4.3 is ferrite. Austenitic stainless steel heated to a temperature above the gamma range will tend to decompose to ferrite, some of which may be retained when the alloy is subsequently cooled. Further, an austenitic alloy whose composition is just sufficient to ensure the austenitic structure at room temperature (at point P on Fig. 4.4) may partially decompose as a result of cold work. The transformation is similar to a martensitic process and the steel is substantially hardened. Another example is found in some of the ferritic steels. These may, in fact, have a chromium content that does not make them entirely ferritic. Thus they may lie in the alpha-plus-gamma region of Fig. 4.1 and be to some extent heat treatable.

Finally, there are the precipitation-hardening stainless steels. The principle of the precipitation-hardening process has been briefly described in Chapter 3. The effect can be utilized in the austenitic and the martensitic stainless steels and will be considered in more detail later.

The introduction of the precipitation-hardening stainless steels has contributed to a confusion of terminology. Prior to the precipitation-hardening alloys, one could refer to the "heat treatable" class of stainless steels and implicate only those steels that could be quenched to martensite and then tempered. The term "heat treatable" is, in fact, better than "martensitic" because although the steels are martensitic after cooling, they are subsequently tempered and their constitution is no longer martensitic. However, the precipitation-hardening steels also enjoy the privilege of heat treatment, and thus we now have to refer to the quenched-and-tempered class as "martensitic" (even though this is not strictly accurate).

Specifications

Many of the common composition ranges of wrought stainless steels are classified as standard AISI (American Iron and Steel Institute) types. The AISI number contains three digits and designates a specified composition range based on the ladle analysis of the steel. The Society of Automotive Engineers (SAE) uses a five-digit system in which the last three digits correspond to the AISI number. The numbers in either system offer no rational clue as to composition except that the austenitic series in the AISI system begins with the number 3; the manganese-substituted austenitic steels begin with a 2 (there are only two such standard steels); both ferritic and martensitic classes in the AISI system begin with the number 4, and the lower numbers in the martensitic class have a lower carbon content.

Specifications of the Alloy Casting Institute (ACI) refer exclusively to cast alloys, although the compositions of some of the ACI alloys approximate wrought alloy compositions. The American Society for Testing and Materials (ASTM) calls for requirements in addition to composition (mechanical properties, heat treatments, testing procedures). Table 4-1 shows the correlation between AISI and SAE numbers and also the equivalence between steels with these specifications and the specifications of ACI and ASTM.

Table 4.1. Correlation of Specifications for Stainless Steels

Wrought alloys			Cast alloys		
AISI	SAE	ASTM	SAE	ACI	ASTM
Martensitic					
403	51403	Plate, sheet, strip: A176; bars, billets: A276	....	....	....
410	51410	Plate, sheet, strip: A176, A240; bars, billets: A276; pipe, tube: A268	60410	CA-15	A296
414	51414	Bars, billets: A276	....	....	....
416, 416Se	51416, 51416Se	Bars, billets: A276	....	....	....
420	51420	Bars, billets: A276	60420	CA-40	....
431	51431	Bars, billets: A276	....	....	....
440A, 440B 440C	....	Bars, billets: A276	....	....	A296
Ferritic					
405	51405	Plate, sheet, strip: A240; bars, billets: A276; pipe, tube: A268	....	....	A351
430, 430F, 430SeF	51430, 51430F, 51430SeF	Plate, sheet, strip: A176, A240; bars, billets: A276; pipe, tube: A268	....	....	....
442	51442	Plate, sheet, strip: A176; bars, billets: A276; pipe, tube: A268	60442	CB-30	A296
446	51446	Plate, sheet, strip: A176; bars, billets: A276; pipe, tube: A268	70446	HC	A297

(*Table continued on next page.*)

Table 4.1. Correlation of Specifications for Stainless Steels (Continued)

Wrought alloys			Cast alloys		
AISI	SAE	ASTM	SAE	ACI	ASTM
		Austenitic			
301	30301	Plate, sheet, strip: A167, A264 (clad)	....	....	....
302	30302	Plate, sheet, strip: A167, A240, A264 (clad); bars, billets: A276, A314	....	CF-20	A296
302B	30302B	Plate, sheet, strip: A167; bars, billets: A276, A314	....	HF	A297
303, 303Se	30303, 30303Se	Bars, billets: A276, A314; nuts, bolts: A194, A320	....	CF-16F	A296
304, 304L	30304, 30304L	Plate, sheet, strip: A167, A177, A240, A264; bars, billets: A276, A314; pipe, tube: A213, A249, A269, A270, A271, A312, A358, A376; nuts, bolts: A193, A194, A320; forgings, fittings: A182, A336	60304, 60304L	CF-8, CF-3	A296, A351
305	30305	Plate, sheet, strip: A240; bars, billets: A314; pipe, tube: A249	....	....	....
308	30308	Plate, sheet, strip: A167, A264; bars, billets: A276, A314; welding electrodes: A298	....	....	....
309, 309S	30309, 30309S	Plate, sheet, strip: A167, A240, A264; bars, billets: A276, A314; pipe, tube: A249, A312, A358; welding electrodes: A298	60309, 70309	CH-20, HH	A296, A297, A351
310, 310S	30310, 30310S	Plate, sheet, strip: A167, A240, A264; bars, billets: A276, A314; pipe, tube: A213, A249, A312, A358; forgings, fittings: A182, A336; welding electrodes: A298	60310, 70310	CK-20, HK	A296, A297, A351

(*Table continued on next page.*)

Table 4.1. Correlation of Specifications for Stainless Steels (Continued)

	Wrought alloys			Cast alloys	
AISI	SAE	ASTM	SAE	ACI	ASTM
		Austenitic (Continued)			
314	30314	Bars, billets: A314	....	....	....
316 316L	30316, 30316L	Plate, sheet, strip: A167, A240, A264; bars, billets: A276, A314; pipe, tube: A213, A249, A269, A312, A358, A376; nuts, bolts: A193; forgings, fittings: A182, A336; welding electrodes: A298	60316, 60316L	CF-3M, CF-8M, CF-12M	A296, A351
317	30317	Plate, sheet, strip: A240; bars, billets: A314; pipe, tube: A249, A269, A312; welding electrodes: A298	60317	CG-8M	A296
321	30321	Plate, sheet, strip: A167, A240, A264; bars, billets: A276, A314; pipe, tube: A213, A249, A269, A271, A312, A358, A376; nuts, bolts: A193, A194, A320; forgings, fittings: A182, A336	....	....	....
347	30347	Plate, sheet, strip: A167, A240, A264; bars, billets: A276, A314; pipe, tube: A213, A249, A269, A271, A298, A358, A376; nuts, bolts: A193, A194, A320; forgings, fittings: A182, A336; welding electrodes: A298	60347	CF-8C	A296, A351
348	30348	Plate, sheet, strip: A240; bars, billets: A276, A314; pipe, tube: A213, A249, A269, A358, A376; nuts, bolts: A320	....	....	....

(*Table continued on next page.*)

Table **4.1.** Correlation of Specifications for Stainless Steels (Continued)

	Wrought alloys			Cast alloys	
AISI	SAE	ASTM	SAE	ACI	ASTM
		Austenitic (Continued)			
		Manganese-Substituted Austenitic			
201	30201	....	....	....	....
202	30202	....	....	....	....
		Precipitation-Hardening			
630	....	Bars, forgings: A461	....	....	....
631	....	Bars, forgings: A461	....	....	....
632	....	Bars, forgings: A461	....	....	....
633	....	Bars, forgings: A461	....	....	....
634	....	Bars, forgings: A461	....	....	....

Martensitic Stainless Steels

Martensitic stainless steels fall into two main groups that are associated with two ranges of mechanical properties: low-carbon materials with maximum hardness of (about) Rockwell C 45 and higher-carbon materials, which can be hardened to Rockwell C 60. (The maximum hardness of both groups in the annealed condition is about Rockwell C 24). Although we will modify this simplicity later, it is convenient to think of steels in the martensitic class as falling on one side or the other of a 0.15% carbon content. The low carbon content must be associated with lower chromium (because if the chromium content is raised the steel will be ferritic at all temperatures and will not be amenable to heat treatment). At higher carbon levels the chromium content can be raised—to about 18%. However, if the high-carbon stainless steels are tempered, the amount of chromium carbide that precipitates is significantly large; hence there are local depletions of chromium in the vicinity of the precipitate and the corrosion resistance suffers. Therefore, the high-carbon grades are not usually tempered. Table 4.2 gives compositions and mechanical properties of the martensitic class.

In the low-carbon steels of the martensitic class, 410 is the progenitor, the basic type. It has a close relation in 416, which has a similar composition except for additions to make it machinable. And there is a rather superior cousin, 403, which has an identical composition (except for a narrower permitted chromium range) and can be more carefully produced to conform to the description "turbine quality." The properties, performance, heat treatment and fabrication of these three steels are similar—with the exception of the easier machinability of 416.

The high-carbon members of the martensitic class are those with the AISI designation 440. This grade is divided into three subgrades, whose difference lies in an increasing carbon content from 440A to 440B to 440C. A more machinable grade, 440F falls into the same general group.

While this fulfills our earlier threat to divide the martensitic stainless steels into high-carbon and low-carbon groups, we have (as always seems to be the case when neat categorizations are attempted) a couple of non-conformists. 420 (and its machinable counterpart 420F) require that the carbon content is over 0.12%. Although this appears to leave the composition wide open, 420 is usually made to a carbon specification between 0.3 and 0.4%. This steel is the original *cutlery grade* of stainless. While it will not harden to such high values as will the higher-carbon 440, it can be tempered without substantial loss of corrosion resistance, and hence a combination of hardness with adequate ductility (suitable for cutlery) can be attained.

The second kind of odd-ball is provided by the addition of small quantities of nickel to the basic composition. The addition (1.25 to 2.50%) is not sufficient to produce an austenitic stainless steel; it is, however, sufficient to increase the hardenability of the steel. Two martensitic stainless steels, conforming to AISI specifications 414 and 431, contain nickel, and they differ only in the maximum carbon allowed (see Table 4.2) and the correspondingly higher chromium content that is permissible with a higher carbon level. These compositions, which are used less on the North American continent than in Europe, are partially austenitic after quenching.

Thus we can place the martensitic stainless steels into the following groups: (*a*) low-carbon; (*b*) low-carbon, nickel-bearing; (*c*) high-carbon; (*d*) medium-carbon. The steels in all of these groups except the high-carbon group can be quenched and tempered; the steels in the high-carbon group can be quenched but cannot usually be tempered. The steels in the first three of these groups can have enhanced machinability by appropriate alloy additions.

Martensitic stainless steels can also be made in precipitation-hardening grades. However, it is less confusing to deal with these alloys under the general category of precipitation-hardening stainless steels, than to intrude the specific martensitic type of age-hardening stainless here. Therefore, the precipitation-hardening grades will be included in a later section.

Embrittlement. Martensitic stainless steels are subject to temper brittleness when they are tempered in the range 800 to 1050 F after quenching, and there is, therefore, some difficulty in attaining the mechanical properties required and simultaneously avoiding low notch ductility. The effect of tempering in this range is shown in the graphs that are presented in our discussions of specific grades.

Table 4.2. Nominal Compositions and Room-Temperature

AISI type	Nominal composition(a), %	Condition
403	11.5–13.0 Cr, 0.15 C, 1.0 Mn, 0.5 Si, 0.04 P, 0.03 S	Annealed Quenched and tempered Cold worked
410	11.5–13.5 Cr, 0.15 C, 1.0 Mn, 1.0 Si, 0.04 P, 0.03 S	Annealed Quenched and tempered Cold worked
414	11.5–13.5 Cr, 1.25–2.50 Ni, 0.15 C, 1.0 Mn, 1.0 Si, 0.04 P, 0.03 S	Annealed Quenched and tempered Cold worked
416(b)	12.0–14.0 Cr, 0.15 C, 1.25 Mn, 1.0 Si, 0.06 P, 0.15 S min, 0.6 Mo (optional)	Annealed Quenched and tempered Cold worked
420	12.0–14.0 Cr, 0.15 C min, 1.0 Mn, 1.0 Si, 0.04 P, 0.03 S	Annealed Quenched and tempered Cold worked
431	15.0–17.0 Cr, 1.25–2.50 Ni, 0.20 C, 1.0 Mn, 1.0 Si, 0.04 P, 0.03 S	Annealed Quenched and tempered Cold worked
440A	16.0–18.0 Cr, 0.60–0.75 C, 1.0 Mn, 1.0 Si, 0.04 P, 0.03 S, 0.75 Mo	Annealed Quenched and tempered
440B	16.0–18.0 Cr, 0.75–0.95 C, 1.0 Mn, 1.0 Si, 0.04 P, 0.03 S, 0.75 Mo	Annealed Quenched and tempered
440C	16.0–18.0 Cr, 0.95–1.20 C, 1.0 Mn, 1.0 Si, 0.04 P, 0.03 S, 0.75 Mo	Annealed Quenched and tempered

(a) Unless otherwise indicated, single figures are maximums.
(b) 416Se has a similar composition, except for a minimum of 0.15% Se.

A quite distinct kind of embrittlement that may arise is due to hydrogen. Hydrogen, acquired during melting, heat treatment, or pickling and electrochemical processing, reduces the ductility of the steel. While temper brittleness is shown by a sharp drop in impact values, hydrogen embrittlement reveals itself during slower deformation. Furnace-atmosphere control can eliminate the problem during heat treatment, but hydrogen absorption cannot always be avoided during chemical and electrochemical treatments. However, the hydrogen can be subsequently removed by heating the steel. Even at temperatures as low as 200 F much hydrogen is driven out. However, de-embrittling treatment of high strength steels involves baking for several hours at temperatures between 400 and 700 F.

Low-Carbon Steels: AISI 403, 410, and 416. While these steels are usually used in a hardened condition, their annealed properties are of sig-

Mechanical Properties of Martensitic Stainless Steels

Yield strength, 1000 psi	Ultimate tensile strength, 1000 psi	Elong in 2 in., %	Hardness		Room-temp Izod, ft-lb	AISI type
			Bhn	Rockwell		
40	75	30	155	B82	100	403
60–150	90–190	30–15	180–390	B89–C41	100–20	
60–100	75–115	25–15	170–235	....	....	
40	75	30	155	B82	100	410
60–150	90–190	30–15	180–390	B89–C41	100–20	
60–100	75–115	25–15	170–235	....	....	
100	120	20	245	B95	60	414
105–150	120–200	20–15	260–415	C24–43	80–40	
110–130	120–140	15–10	250–315	....	....	
40	75	30	155	B82	80	416
60–150	90–190	25–10	180–390	B89–C41	60–20	
60–100	75–115	20–10	170–235	....	....	
50	95	25	200	B92	60	420
80–200	110–240	25–5	250–550	C20–55	Low	
80–100	100–120	20–15	....	....	....	
100	125	20	260	C24	70	431
100–180	140–220	20–10	270–440	C25–45	70–25	
110–140	130–150	15–10	270–325	....	....	
60	105	20	215	B95	Low	440A
80–240	120–260	10–2	To 570	To C56	Low	
65	110	15	225	B97	Low	440B
90–250	130–270	10–2	To 600	To C60	Low	
70	115	10	230	B98	Low	440C
90–270	130–280	10–2	To 600	To C60	Low	

nificance during forming processes. Minimum hardness is acquired by full annealing (soak at 1550 to 1600 F for about 2 hrs per inch of thickness; cool to 1100 F at a rate not exceeding 50 F per hour; air cool). This treatment is, of course, predicated by the necessity of avoiding the formation of martensite during cooling. Properties of the fully annealed material are given in Table 4.2.

Alternatively, if partial softening and better machinability are required, the steels can be subcritically annealed at 1350 to 1450 F for several hours, to effect the fully tempered condition, and air cooled. Such a treatment gives a hardness of about Rockwell B 90, with correspondingly higher strength.

For the development of high strength, the steels of this group are air cooled (or oil quenched) after soaking at 1700 to 1850 F for (about) 1 hr per inch of thickness. The hardenability of the martensitic stainless steels is sufficiently great that air cooling effects an adequate quench. However, oil quenching is quicker and may be more convenient, but it involves a risk of distortion. Tempering should immediately follow the air or oil quench. And, if the steel is not to be tempered (that is, if it is to be used at maximum hardness) it should be stress relieved at about 600 F for 3 hr.

The effect of tempering on tensile properties and hardness is shown in Fig. 4.5. The tempering range 900 to 1100 F is associated with a very rapid drop of strength and hardness, and the tempered values will depend upon the exact composition of the steel and heat treatment variables.

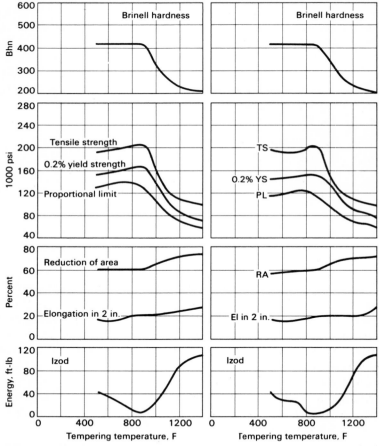

Fig. 4.5. Effect of austenitizing and tempering temperatures on room-temperature mechanical properties of 410. Austenitized (left) at 1700 F and (right) at 1850 F for 30 min; oil quenched to 150 to 200 F; double stress relieved at 350 F for 15 min; water quenched; tempered 2 hr

Therefore, it is as well to temper at a slightly lower temperature than that indicated by the graphs: if a test shows that the steel is too hard, then the piece can be retempered at a higher temperature.

The graph of Izod impact values plotted against tempering temperature shows that 410 is susceptible to temper brittleness—as, indeed, are all the martensitic stainless steels. Thus, if notch sensitivity is to be avoided, the steels must not be tempered between 800 and 1050 F. At higher tempering temperatures the substantial formation of carbides reduces the corrosion resistance. Hence, to make the best of rather frustrating circumstances, tempering is performed as little above the embrittlement range as possible.

Like heat treatable machinery steels, martensitic stainless steels have a crystal structure that is (roughly) body-centered cubic; thus they have a ductile-brittle transition temperature. In simple tension, the temperature at which such a steel becomes brittle is very low (about −300 F). But the *notch* ductility (customarily determined by the impact test) drops very suddenly at temperatures nearer room temperature, as Fig. 4.6 shows.

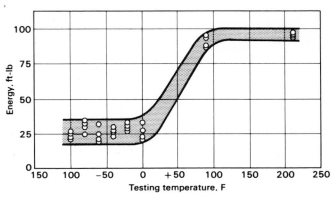

Fig. 4.6. Izod data for 410 after quenching from 1800 F and tempering at 1150 F. (*Bhn 228*)

The precise transition temperature depends upon the heat treatment and composition (as well as upon steelmaking-practice variables). Steel of 410 specification, for example, passes through sharply changing Charpy and Izod values between −50 and +50 F, and differences in constitution (due to compositional and steelmaking variables) may move the transition temperature substantially. The fact is that in any condition, notch ductility of 410 may be low at temperatures just below room temperature, and the harder the steel (in the quenched-and-tempered condition) the higher will be its transition temperature. Clearly, if notch ductility is critical at temperatures at, or below, room temperature, and the steel is to be used in the hardened condition, careful evaluation is required. The chances are, if the material is to be used much below room temperature, that the quenched-and-tempered 410 grade will not be satisfactory. In the annealed condition a 15 ft-lb Charpy value can be maintained at temperatures down to (about) −100 F, but the use of annealed material should be be questioned, because other classes of stainless are probably more appropriate.

Although we have lumped 410, 403 and 416 together, the actual measurement of energy absorbed in 416 (the machinable grade) is less than it is in 410 and 403.

A hardened steel is not usually used at temperatures above the temperature at which it was tempered. 410, or more usually 403 (turbine quality), develops properties after tempering at 1100 F that make it adequate for use at temperatures up to 1000 F. If strength can be sacrificed

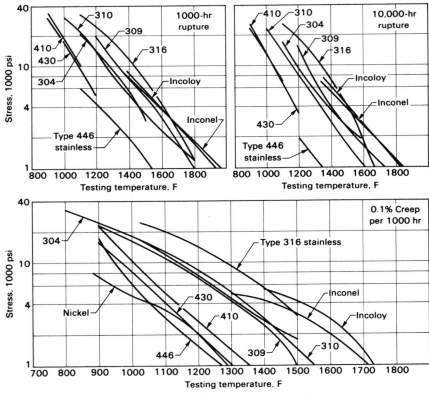

Fig. 4.7. Creep and creep-rupture comparisons

(and if high-temperature corrosion is not a problem), however, higher-temperature operation is possible. The room-temperature properties of the 1100 F tempered material have been shown in Fig. 4.5. These properties are maintained in short-term tests up to (about) 600 F. However, common service of this type of stainless in turbine blades, valves, and fittings, involves protracted time at temperature. Creep data are therefore required. Figure 4.7 shows creep and creep-rupture properties for 410 compared with other stainless steels and heat-resisting materials. More data are given in Fig. 4.8. At elevated temperature (we remind ourselves) notch ductility is high.

The fatigue properties of the martensitic stainless steels, as of all steels, depend not only upon their heat treatment but upon the design into which they are constructed. The effect of a notch in a structure or of a corrosive environment can do much more to reduce the fatigue limit of any steel than the metallurgical engineer can accommodate by increasing the basic fatigue resistance of a material by alloying and heat treatment.

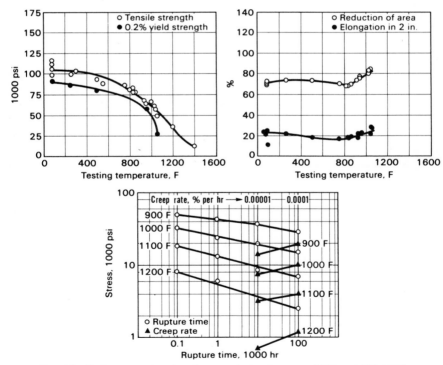

Fig. 4.8. High-temperature data for quenched-and-tempered 403 and 410 (12% chromium). (Six heats)

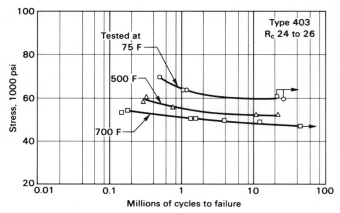

Fig. 4.9. Fatigue data for quenched-and-tempered 403. (Rockwell C 24 to 26)

Figure 4.9 gives fatigue data for 403 (turbine quality) at three testing temperatures. The samples in this test were smooth and polished, and the atmosphere was air. A notch reduces the fatigue limit to the extent that it builds up a stress concentration at its root; an environment reduces the fatigue limit to the extent that it permits corrosion. Cycling speed, specimen size, and history also affect fatigue properties. Therefore any data can be used as only a rough guide. For example, while the figure of 45,000 psi might seem a reasonable one on which to design a turbine blade operating at 700 F, the effect of steam corrosion, and possibly water corrosion, might reduce the value to 30,000 psi, and design considerations (a section change at the root of the blade) might further reduce the value to less than 10,000 psi.

Nickel-Bearing Low-Carbon Steels: AISI 414 and 431. These steels are usually put in a soft condition by subcritical annealing between 1150 and 1225 F for 431 and between 1225 and 1300 F for 414.

Mechanical properties and response to heat treatment are very similar to those of 410. The addition of nickel serves two purposes: (*a*) it improves corrosion resistance in specific environments—in neutral chlorides and in feebly oxidizing acids; the nickel addition in 431 permits a higher chromium content than in the 410 grade—and this, in itself, is advantageous; (*b*) the notch toughness of the heat treated steels is improved.

Figure 4.10 compares the properties of the nickel-free with the nickel-containing martensitic stainless steels. An upward trend in strength in the nickel-bearing steels is measured at tempering temperatures above 1250 F. This is possibly because both 414 and 431 are partially austenitic after air cooling. Then, when carbides precipitate during tempering, the composition of the austenite changes (through a reduction in chromium and car-

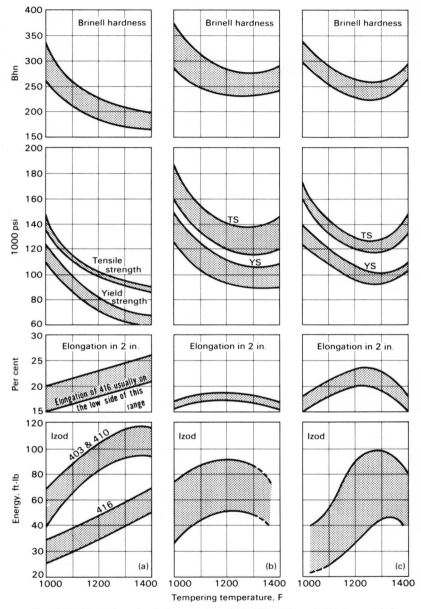

Fig. 4.10. Typical mechanical properties of (a) 403, 410, and 416 (non-nickel-bearing), (b) 431 (nickel-bearing), and (c) 414 (nickel-bearing) in the tempered condition. All values are expressed as approximate ranges. Variations occur because of differences in analysis, as-quenched hardness, and time at drawing temperature. Data from Allegheny Ludlum Steel Corp.

bon) to permit its subsequent transformation to martensite during cooling to room temperature from the tempering temperature.

An example of variations in data is reflected by comparing Fig. 4.10 (which shows an upswing in tensile properties as the tempering temperature reaches 1300 F) with Fig. 4.11. While the data in Fig. 4.11 do not extend beyond the 1300 F tempering temperature, there is little promise of a subsequent increase in strength. Further, Fig. 4.11 draws our attention to the susceptibility to temper embrittlement in the tempering temperature

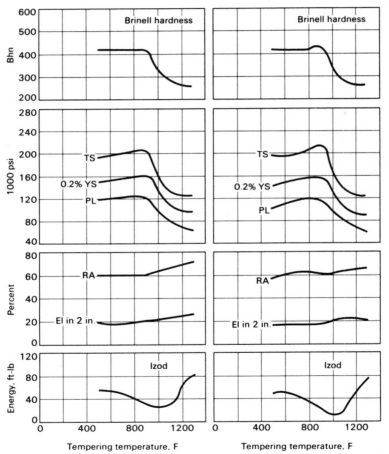

Fig. 4.11. *Effect of austenitizing and tempering temperatures on mechanical properties of 414. Austenitized (left) at 1700 F and (right) at 1900 F for 30 min; oil quenched to 150 to 200 F; double stress relieved at 350 F for 15 min; water quenched; tempered 2 hr*

range 800 to 1050 F. While variations in mechanical properties values are disconcerting, they must be expected in materials that are supplied to a fairly wide range of composition. However, whatever the range of composition and its effect upon strength values, temper brittleness is to be expected.

High-temperature properties of 414 are given in Fig. 4.12, and it will be noted that rupture time for 414 is similar to the nickel-free 410 grade (Fig. 4.8).

Improved high-temperature properties are obtained by the addition of tungsten, molybdenum, and vanadium to the 12% chromium composition, to produce a nonstandard type that is designated 422. This alloy is one of many variants on the 12% composition, designed to give better high-temperature properties.

High-Carbon Steels: AISI 440. While these steels are usually used in a hardened condition, minimal hardness for forming is obtained by a full

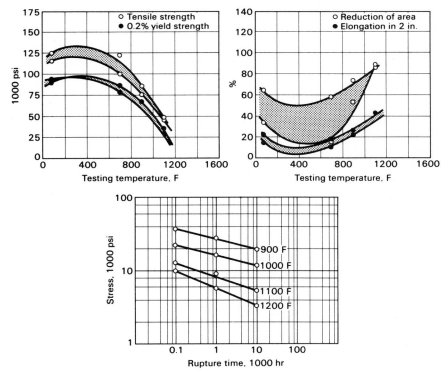

Fig. 4.12. High-temperature data for quenched-and-tempered 414 (12% chromium, 2% nickel). (Two heats)

anneal (hold at 1650 F; cool slowly to 1100 F; air cool). Partial softening can be effected (as for 410) by holding at 1450 F.

Mechanical properties of the fully annealed material are given in Table 4.2. Partial softening, through subcritical annealing, results in a hardness a few points higher, with correspondingly higher strength, lower ductility, and better machinability.

For hardening, the high-carbon grades should be taken to 1450 F, soaked, and then heated to 1825 to 1925 F and air or oil quenched. However, austenite (the high-temperature phase) may be retained at room temperature, and subsequent isothermal transformation to martensite (with accompanying size changes and cracking) may occur at room temperature. This danger can be eliminated by one of two procedures: (*a*) a subzero quench (to about -100 F), at which temperature sensibly all austenite transforms; (*b*) a stress relief at 700 F.

For the quenched and stress-relieved condition, values of yield strength and ultimate tensile strength reach 250,000 to 275,000 psi, and hardness varies from Rockwell C 50 in 440A to Rockwell C 60 in 440C. But the steel is brittle (impact values are only a few foot pounds at room temperature), and these strength values are therefore not applicable. If the 440 grade is tempered to improve its ductility, then it suffers a marked loss of corrosion resistance, and the required mechanical properties are more satisfactorily realized by 410. In short, 440 is useful where high hardness and wear resistance are required in a stainless material; these are obtained in the quenched and stress-relieved material. But the properties that 440 offers after tempering are not attractive.

Medium-Carbon Steels: AISI 420 (and 420F). The heat treatments—annealing, subcritical annealing, and hardening—are similar to those already described for 410. Variation with tempering temperature of yield strength, ultimate tensile strength, elongation, and hardness are given in Fig. 4.13. The range of temper embrittlement will be seen once more.

In this steel, one tries to get the better of two worlds: the hardness associated with 440 and the ductility of 410. Because it is used in the tempered condition, some attempt is made to improve corrosion resistance by an increase in chromium content over that of 410; however, the increase cannot be great (because the steel will become ferritic) and, in fact, the ranges of chromium content in 410 and 420 substantially overlap (see Table 4.2). Further, the carbon specification of 420 simply calls for a 0.15% minimum. In fact, 420 usually contains 0.20 to 0.40% C. We referred earlier to the delicate position of the martensitic stainless steels and the fact that we are lucky to have them at all. In the 420 grade, we are really playing it as fine as we can—the maximum carbon content to offer adequate hardness, with sufficient chromium to give corrosion resistance

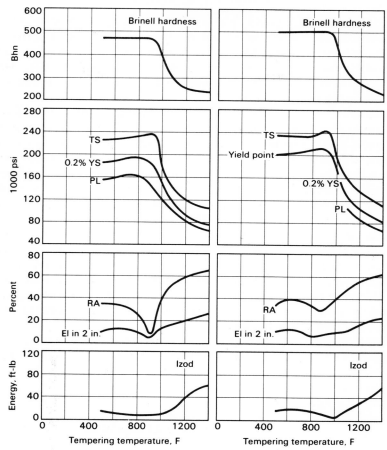

Fig. 4.13. Effect of austenitizing and tempering temperatures on mechanical properties of 420. Austenitized (left) at 1700 F and (right) at 1875 F for 30 min; oil quenched to 150 to 200 F; double stress relieved at 350 F for 15 min; water quenched; tempered 2 hr

in the tempered material, yet not so much chromium that the steel becomes ferritic and non-heat-treatable.

The notch ductility of 420 in the hardened condition is not high. At a hardness level of Rockwell C 49 (yield strength of 150,000 psi, ultimate tensile strength of 175,000 psi) its Charpy values are between 5 and 15 ft-lb at all temperatures between −100 and 200 F. However, the steel is not intended for use where high notch ductility is required. At some sacrifice of strength, it offers more toughness than 440—in fact, it offers the combination of mechanical properties that makes it a *cutlery stainless.*

Ferritic Stainless Steels

This class of stainless steels is sensibly ferritic at all temperatures and therefore cannot be strengthened by heat treatment—although we will see that some of the "ferritic" grades do undergo some transformation. However, even these are substantially ferritic—body-centered cubic and magnetic below their Curie temperature.

Table 4.3 shows compositions and mechanical properties of the ferritic stainless steels. These steels do not possess a particularly high strength; their ductility is rather low; their notch ductility is poor. The strength of this class can be increased by heat treatment only if the chromium-carbon balance is such that some austenite is formed at temperature. Strength can be increased by cold working, but the effects of cold work are much less marked than in the austenitic grade, which is discussed later. Because the ductility, and hence the formability, of the ferritic steels is limited, they are usually used in the annealed condition, where they fully develop their most valuable characteristic: good corrosion resistance. It is when corrosion resistance and economy count that the ferritic stainless steels find their place. In general, as the chromium content is increased, corrosion resistance is improved, but costs are higher, there is less chance of hardening during cooling, and forming is more difficult because of reduced ductility and notch ductility.

In addition to low ductility, ferritic stainless steels suffer from problems associated with (*a*) grain growth, (*b*) 885 F embrittlement, (*c*) sigma-phase embrittlement, and (*d*) sensitization. We are, thankfully, spared temper embrittlement, because the class is not heat treatable, and hydrogen embrittlement rarely occurs.

Table 4.3. Nominal Compositions and Room-Temperature

AISI type	Nominal composition(a), % .	Condition
405	11.5–14.5 Cr, 0.08 C, 1.0 Mn, 1.0 Si, 0.04 P, 0.03 S, 0.1–0.3 Al	Annealed Cold worked
430	14.0–18.0 Cr, 0.12 C, 1.0 Mn, 1.0 Si, 0.04 P, 0.03 S	Annealed Cold worked
430F	14.0–18.0 Cr, 0.12 C, 1.25 Mn, 1.0 Si, 0.06 P, 0.15 S min, 0.60 Mo (optional)	Annealed Cold worked
442	18.0–23.0 Cr, 0.20 C, 1.0 Mn, 1.0 Si, 0.04 P, 0.03 S	Annealed Cold worked
446	23.0–27.0 Cr, 0.20 C, 1.5 Mn, 1.0 Si, 0.04 P, 0.03 S, 0.25 N	Annealed Cold worked

(a) Unless otherwise indicated, single figures are maximums.

Grain Growth. If in the heat treatable grades, as in the plain carbon steels, a coarse-grain size is developed by some accident (let us suppose) or by unavoidable circumstances, this can be rectified by heating the steel to just above its transformation temperature, where fine-grained austenite will form. The fine-grained austenite will produce fine-grained decomposition products on cooling. But the ferritic stainless steels are at all temperatures ferritic: their grain size increases as their temperature increases, and they undergo no transformation. The only means of refining the grain size of a ferritic stainless steel is by cold work and subsequent annealing — and this is not practical in many fabrication processes.

The problems associated with grain growth are displayed in welding, when the heat-affected zone suffers. And, with the large grain size, a loss of ductility — and particularly of notch ductility — occurs.

885 F Embrittlement. In Europe this is called 475 brittleness, and when we are sensible enough to use the Celsius scale, we will use the same name. But for the present, it is 885 F embrittlement.

Figure 4.14 shows the variation of hardness of ferritic stainless steels with holding temperature. The hardness peak at (about) 900 F is associated with a corresponding loss of ductility. Elongation figures in tension for ferritic stainless steels are not particularly high (see Table 4.3) for the strength level. Notch ductility is poor. After 885 F embrittlement, ductility and notch ductility are so low that the steel is generally inapplicable. The effect can occur not only through holding the ferritic steel at (about) 885 F, but through slow cooling from higher temperatures.

The mechanism of this phenomenon does not appear to be understood, but the effect becomes more pronounced as the chromium content in-

Mechanical Properties of Ferritic Stainless Steels

Yield strength, 1000 psi	Ultimate tensile strength, 1000 psi	Elong in 2 in., %	Hardness		Room-temp Izod, ft-lb	AISI type
			Bhn	Rockwell		
40	70	30	150	B80	25	405
60–120	90–130	20–10	...	...	...	
45	75	30	155	B82	50–5	430
65–125	90–130	20–2	...	...	...	
55	80	25	170	B86	50–5	430F
70–100	85–115	18–10	...	...	...	
45	80	20	170	B86	Low	442
70–100	90–110	20–15	...	...	...	
50	80	23	170	B86	Low	446
70–100	90–110	20–15	...	...	...	

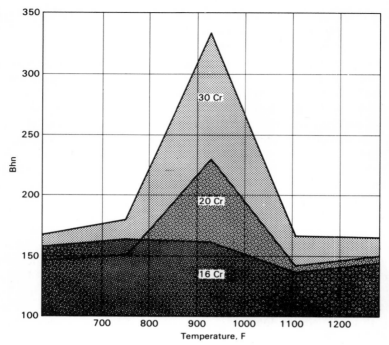

*Fig. 4.14. Effect of 885 F embrittlement on hardness. Alloy was held at tem-
perature indicated for 500 hr*

creases. However, any embrittlement that has been suffered can be
removed by subsequent heating to 1100 F and rapidly cooling the steel.

Sigma-Phase Embrittlement. This can be rationalized to the extent
that the sigma phase, a hard, brittle material, is identifiable under the
microscope and by x-ray diffraction. It forms slowly, at temperatures
between 1000 and 1600 F, first developing at grain boundaries. Figure
4.15 shows the region of temperatures and compositions over which sigma
is an equilibrium phase. The diagram shows that we should not expect
any development of this phase at chromium contents below (about) 20%
chromium. However, sigma embrittlement may occur in weldments and
castings containing less than this chromium content, probably because the
chromium is not homogeneously distributed.

The sigma phase takes so long to form that it is not usually a heat
treatment problem: it arises during high-temperature service. And while
this type of embrittlement is essentially associated with the ferritic stainless steels, it may arise in the austenitic class—and will be mentioned
again when the austenitic stainless steels are described.

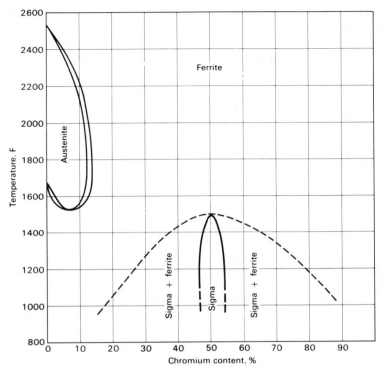

Fig. 4.15. Sigma-phase region in phase diagram of iron-chromium alloys

If sigma-phase embrittlement occurs, it can be removed by dissolving sigma at temperatures above 1650 F. Rapid cooling is recommended in order that 885 F brittleness is avoided.

Sensitization. The problem of sensitization is probably most familiar as it applies to austenitic stainless steels—and it will be discussed in the appropriate section. However, sensitization of ferritic stainless steels is not uncommon, although the circumstances under which it arises are quite different from those that pertain to the austenitic class. In the sensitized condition the steel will be attacked at its grain boundaries by corrosive mediums that it can normally tolerate, and it will eventually disintegrate.

In the ferritic stainless steels sensitization is mot likely to occur when the chromium content is greater than about 16%, and the condition is induced by rapid cooling from temperatures above 1700 F. Hence its most common occurrence is immediately adjacent to welds. Plate and sections that are cooled after rolling usually lose heat sufficiently slowly to avoid the effect.

Sensitization can be detected by submitting a sample of the steel to boiling nitric acid (65%) for several days, after which time attack is obvious to the naked eye. It can be removed by heating the steel to about 1400 F for an hour or so followed by air cooling. Although this temperature falls within the sigma formation range, the short time of the heat treatment is not sufficient to permit sigma formation, and the rate of air cooling is great enough to avoid 885 F embrittlement.

The Truly Ferritic Steel: AISI 446. While other ferritic stainless steels are much more commonly used, 446 is the honest member of the family: it is ferritic at all temperatures to the melting range. But, in addition to the brittle ranges that it suffers (the family disease), this particular fellow is not very ductile, and is certainly not at all notch ductile, at room temperature. For this reason it is usually warmed to about 300 F before "cold forming."

Of the ferritic stainless steels, it is perhaps the most difficult to handle because the problems of embrittlement are worse at this higher chromium level, the poor room-temperature notch ductility complicates fabrication, and the difficulties of grain growth are ever present. In order to minimize the grain growth, nitrogen can be added to the composition: Table 4.3 shows that a rather high maximum (0.25%) is permitted.

As we have already pointed out, ferritic stainless steels are not generally used where mechanical strength is a prime consideration. However, with all the stainless steels, strength at temperature and resistance to creep are significant. Data for 446 have been compared with data for other stainless steels in Fig. 4.7.

Muffler Alloys. Recently, new grades of ferritic stainless steels containing only 11% chromium have been developed for automotive exhaust mufflers and tail pipes. The carbon content of these alloys, which is held to a 0.045% maximum, permits such a low chromium content to offer passivity, and, aided by the addition of ferritizers such as titanium, ensures a nonhardenable structure. Hence the dangers of cracking in the heat-affected zone are minimized. In the production of mufflers, resistance welding techniques are employed, which would offer difficulties in the standard ferritic grades other than the high-priced 446.

Slightly Hardenable Steels: AISI 430 and 430F. The constitution of 430, the most common of the ferritic stainless steels, is not strictly ferritic because on heating to above 1500 F austenite may appear. During cooling, the austenite will transform to martensite, and, if the steel is cooled from 1800 F, hardness values up to Rockwell C 30 may develop. For maximum ductility the steel is heated to a temperature (1400 to 1500 F) below the critical temperature and air cooled, or, if the annealing temperature is above critical (that is, above about 1500 F), furnace cooling to 1100 F followed by air cooling is necessary.

In the annealed condition, this steel offers the best combination of properties of the ferritic class. It is more formable than 446—although if its chromium content is at the high end of the range, preheating is recommended. Easier fabrication offsets its lower corrosion resistance and lower annealed strength. It becomes lustrous on cold rolling, without buffing. Consequently, this steel is used in substantial quantities for automotive trim, and it represents about 95% of the entire ferritic stainless production in the United States.

430 like the other ferritic stainless steels has poor low-temperature notch ductility. A marked increase in yield and ultimate tensile strength accompanies the reduction of tensile ductility and notch ductility at very low temperatures. High-temperature data for 430 have been compared with data for other stainless steels in Fig. 4.7. A comparison with 446 shows that the additional chromium in 446 does little for creep properties.

There are two types of modification of the 430 composition. First, there are the machinable grades (430F), which contain a number of possible additions. A resulfurized grade contains a minimum of 0.15% sulfur and possibly small amounts of molybdenum and zirconium; the selenium grade contains a minimum of 0.15% selenium (sulfur is held at the conventional 0.03%). Second, there is a modification that involves the addition of a titanium stabilizer—this is a nonstandard grade. We will see, when we discuss sensitization of austenitic stainless steels in a later section (p. 52), that titanium, being a carbide former, reduces susceptibility to grain-boundary corrosion. While this is certainly the effect of a titanium addition to the austenitic steels, the effect in ferritic grades is to reduce embrittlement in the heat-affected zone of welds, by ensuring a ferritic structure at temperature. Hence the formation on cooling of the rather brittle martensitic structure is avoided. The over-all corrosion resistance is, as it happens, usually lowered by the addition.

Low-Chromium Steel: AISI 405. The chromium content of 405 (11.5 to 13.5%) with 0.08% maximum carbon would normally produce a martensitic structure (although, it must be admitted, not a very hard one). However, by the addition of 0.1 to 0.3% aluminum, the steel is maintained in a ferritic condition. Thus it offers the low chromium of a martensitic grade, without the disadvantages of hardening. The embrittlement problems associated with higher chromium are reduced, and, with adequate corrosion resistance, the alloy offers weldability without subsequent annealing, at low cost.

Nonstandard Steels: AISI 406, 442, and 443. 406, a standard grade until recently, contains 13% chromium and 0.15% maximum carbon. The addition of 3.5 to 4.5% aluminum ensures the complete elimination of possible hardening. 442 and 443 fall between 446 and 430 in chromium content, containing 21% chromium, and compromise the formability, cost, and properties of these two grades. 443 contains 1 to 2% copper, which enhances its resistance to sulfuric acid.

Austenitic Stainless Steels

Like the ferritic grades, the austenitic stainless steels cannot be hardened to form martensite by quenching. Whatever the cooling rate, they are austenitic at room temperature. Nor do they undergo a transformation on heating to temperatures below the melting range. Thus, like the ferritic stainless steels, their grain size cannot be controlled. However, grain growth is not so great a problem.

While the ferritic stainless steels can be strengthened to some extent by cold working, this effect is not great, and its extent is limited by the rather low ductility of the grade. However, the austenitic grades are much more ductile: they can suffer more cold work without breaking, and, further, during cold work, many members of the group undergo a transformation that is, in fact, martensitic. Thus we should expect to find substantial strengthening in many austenitic steels during cold working.

The austenitic stainless grades are easier to weld than the ferritic. Sensitization can be reasonably overcome; the problem of grain growth is not nearly so critical; there are fewer problems of lack of weld ductility. This, with the comparative ease of forming, makes the austenitic stainless steel a reasonable one to handle in the shop.

The production figures shown in Chapter 1 demonstrate the popularity of the austenitic stainless steels. The ferritic grades show their maximum production during shortages of nickel, and their use is greatest in the form of 430 sheet for the automotive industry. If we exclude, for the moment, the specific needs of the automotive business, and assume that nickel is available, then the chances are about 5 to 1 that you will be involved with an austenitic grade. Fortunately it is a fairly easy alloy to understand. The fact that the austenitic stainless steels are (generally) easier to use, that they often show superior corrosion resistance, is consistent with their greater tonnage. But one suspects that there are occasions when their use in preference to a ferritic grade is associated with the comparative wealth of information that is available on the austenitic grades and, perhaps, with the persuasive advertising that pushes them.

Sensitization.   The major pitfall in the austenitic class is the possibility of sensitization. It is much more common in the austenitic steels than in the ferritic — and we should point out immediately that the heat treatment that removes sensitization from a ferritic grade would induce it in an austenitic steel.

The term "weld decay" implies that the phenomenon of sensitization was first observed in the heat-affected zones of welds in austenitic stainless steels. At a distance from the weld corresponding to a temperature during welding of about 1200 F, the weldment showed catastrophic corrosion failure. Examination of the affected region revealed that failure was intercrystalline. Although theories to rationalize the phenomenon tick-tock across the pages of technical journals, we will plump for one that offers an understandable mechanism. First, however, more facts must be presented.

When austenitic stainless steels are heated between 800 and 1500 F, subsequent performance in corrosive environments is marred by intergranular attack. They have become *sensitized*. The most critical temperature is about 1200 F—where holding for only a few seconds may be sufficient to permit subsequent deterioration. In straight-chromium grades similar deterioration is experienced when the holding temperature is 1700 F and above, and the effect seems to be less common. The subsequent comments pertain exclusively to austenitic grades.

On the basis of metallographic studies and the nature of remedial measures, it seems reasonable to suppose that sensitization occurs through chromium impoverishment at a region immediately adjacent to the grain boundaries. Chromium and carbon, originally distributed through the austenitic structure, combine to form chromium carbide. The temperature at which this occurs most rapidly is about 1200 F: at lower temperatures diffusion rates of the atoms are less; at higher temperatures there is an effective reverse process—the decomposition of chromium carbide. The precipitation of the carbide occurs most readily at grain boundaries (although not exclusively so)—for reasons that are fatuous if stated simply and tedious if fully developed.

The formation of chromium carbide requires three atoms of chromium to one atom of carbon. Carbon is a small atom and diffuses rapidly through the austenite crystal; chromium, a bigger atom, diffuses much more slowly. Therefore, while the carbon atoms migrate to the grain boundary from all parts of the crystal, chromium is depleted from more localized regions near the grain boundary, forming an envelope of chromium-depleted material. This region is, therefore, susceptible to corrosion.

An additional feature that perhaps contributes to the corrosion process is the galvanic effect that arises between the precipitated particles of chromium carbide and the austenite around it.

It is possible to pick holes in this rationalization of sensitization, but it is sufficiently accurate to allow us to understand the preventive or remedial measures. These are

1. The sensitized steel can be reheated to temperatures at which the carbides redissolve, and cooled quickly through the sensitizing range. Soaking temperature should be about 2000 F, and cooling should be rapid

Table 4.4. Nominal Compositions and Room Temperature

AISI type	Nominal composition(a), %	Condition(b,c)
201	16–18 Cr, 3.5–5.5 Ni, 0.15 C, 1.0 Si, 5.5–7.5 Mn, 0.06 P, 0.03 S, 0.25 N	Annealed Cold worked
202	17–19 Cr, 4.0–6.0 Ni, 0.15 C, 1.0 Si, 7.5–10 Mn, 0.06 P, 0.03 S, 0.25 N	Annealed
301	16–18 Cr, 6.0–8.0 Ni, 0.15 C, 1.0 Si, 2.0 Mn, 0.045 P, 0.03 S	Annealed Cold worked
302	17–19 Cr, 8.0–10.0 Ni, 0.15 C, 1.0 Si, 2.0 Mn, 0.045 P, 0.03 S	Annealed Cold worked
302B	17–19 Cr, 8.0–10.0 Ni, 0.15 C, 2.0 Mn, 2.0–3.0 Si, 0.045 P, 0.03 S	Annealed
303(d)	17–19 Cr, 8.0–10.0 Ni, 0.15 C, 1.0 Si, 2.0 Mn, 0.20 P, 0.15 S min, 0.60 Mo (optional)	Annealed Cold worked
304(e)	18–20 Cr, 8.0–12.0 Ni, 0.08 C, 1.0 Si, 2.0 Mn, 0.045 P, 0.03 S	Annealed Cold worked
305	17–19 Cr, 10.0–13.0 Ni, 0.12 C, 1.0 Si, 2.0 Mn, 0.045 P, 0.03 S	Annealed
308	19–21 Cr, 10.0–12.0 Ni, 0.08 C, 1.0 Si, 2.0 Mn, 0.045 P, 0.03 S	Annealed Cold worked
309(f)	22–24 Cr, 12.0–15.0 Ni, 0.20 C, 1.0 Si, 2.0 Mn, 0.045 P, 0.03 S	Annealed
310(f)	24–26 Cr, 19–22 Ni, 0.25 C, 1.5 Si, 2.0 Mn, 0.045 P, 0.03 S	Annealed
314	23–26 Cr, 19–22 Ni, 0.25 C, 1.5–3.0 Si, 2.0 Mn, 0.045 P, 0.03 S	Annealed Cold worked
316(e)	16–18 Cr, 10–14 Ni, 0.08 C, 1.0 Si, 2.0 Mn, 0.045 P, 0.03 S, 2.0–3.0 Mo	Annealed Cold worked
317	18–20 Cr, 11–15 Ni, 0.08 C, 1.0 Si, 2.0 Mn, 0.045 P, 0.03 S, 3.0–4.0 Mo	Annealed
321	17–19 Cr, 9–12 Ni, 0.08 C, 1.0 Si, 2.0 Mn, 0.045 P, 0.03 S, Ti = 5 × C min	Annealed Cold worked
347	17–19 Cr, 9–13 Ni, 0.08 C, 1.0 Si, 2.0 Mn, 0.045 P, 0.03 S, Cb + Ta = 10 × C min	Annealed Cold worked
348	17–19 Cr, 9–13 Ni, 0.08 C, 1.0 Si, 2.0 Mn, 0.045 P, 0.03 S, 0.2 Co, Cb + Ta = 10 × C min, but 0.1 Ta max	Annealed

(a) Unless otherwise indicated, single figures are maximums.
(b) Properties given for the cold worked condition are for approximately $\frac{1}{2}$-hard sheet, except for 303, for which properties pertain to cold drawn bar stock.
(c) Austenitic stainless steels are annealed between 1850 and 2050 F.

Mechanical Properties of Austenitic Stainless Steels

Yield strength, 1000 psi	Ultimate tensile strength, 1000 psi	Elong in 2 in., %	Hardness		Room-temp Izod, ft-lb	AISI type
			Bhn	Rockwell		
55	110	50	· · ·	B90	100	201
To 140	To 185	50–8	· · ·	To C41	· · ·	
55	100	50	· · ·	B90	100	202
40	110	60	165	B85	100	301
To 140	To 185	60–8	· · ·	To C41	· · ·	
40	90	55	155	B82	100	302
To 150	To 180	55–10	· · ·	To C35	· · ·	
40	95	50	165	B85	90	302B
35	90	55	160	B84	85	303
To 100	To 180	55–30	To 330	To C35	· · ·	
35	85	55	150	B80	100	304
To 150	To 180	55–10	To 330	To C35	· · ·	
37	85	55	156	B82	100	305
35	85	55	150	B80	100	308
To 150	To 180	55–10	To 330	To C35	· · ·	
40	90	65	165	B85	100	309
40	95	65	170	B87	100	310
50	100	40	180	B90	90	314
To 125	To 150	40–10	· · ·	To C30	· · ·	
35	85	55	150	B80	90	316
To 125	To 150	55–10	To 300	To C30	· · ·	
40	90	55	160	B85	90	317
35	87	55	150	B80	90	321
To 125	To 150	55–10	To 300	To C30	· · ·	
35	92	50	160	B84	90	347
To 125	To 150	50–10	To 300	To C30	· · ·	
35	92	50	160	B84	90	348

(d) 303 Se has similar properties.   The sulfur content is restricted to 0.06% maximum and 0.15% minimum selenium is required.

(e) These alloys are available in extra-low-carbon (L) grades, with a maximum carbon content of 0.03%.   Yield and ultimate tensile strengths are a little lower.

(f) The carbon content of 309S and 310S is restricted to 0.08% maximum; yield and ultimate tensile strengths are lower.

—a water quench if possible. Naturally, this remedial measure is not always applicable.

2.   If the sensitizing range cannot be avoided, a steel of very low carbon content can be used so that the amount of chromium carbide formed, and hence the extent of chromium depletion, are small. The *extra-low-carbon* grades of austenitic stainless steel are designed for this purpose.

3.   One might expect that the use of a steel with a high chromium content would offset the localized chromium loss. While this helps, it is not as advantageous as one might hope—a hole in the sensitization theory we have propounded.

4.   The most popular method is to encourage the formation of some other carbide in the austenitic steels by the addition of elements that are avaricious toward carbon. These elements are (primarily) titanium and columbium. When the austenitic steel is heated in the sensitizing range, the carbon now combines *not* with chromium, but much more rapidly with the *stabilizer*—titanium or columbium. Once the carbon is quickly tied up, chromium has no urge to engage in the carbide-forming business. The relative merits of titanium, columbium and (for special circumstances) tantalum, will be discussed under the specific grades of steel.

Sigma Embrittlement.   Sigma is formed from high-chromium ferrite, and hence we might anticipate that it should not appear in the austenitic alloys. However, some of the austenitic alloys are not entirely austenitic, and, in welding austenitic stainless steels, some ferrite is usually purposely allowed to form. Where this happens the chromium-rich ferrite will, indeed, be susceptible to sigma formation—in the same way that the ferritic steels are susceptible. The problem, when it arises, is usually restricted to welds.

General Classification.   Table 4.4 gives compositions and mechanical properties of the austenitic stainless steels. Table 4.5 gives suggested stress-relieving treatments. The parent of the austenitic class is 302. It is commonly known as 18–8 stainless—a name that is given with less justification to many other steels in the class. Grouped about this alloy are others whose specific applications are better met by an adjusted composition. Thus, as a general classification of the austenitic stainless steels we have (*a*) basic 18–8 stainless steel, (*b*) steels with a higher nickel content to reduce susceptibility to work hardening, (*c*) especially corrosion-resistant austenitic stainless steels, (*d*) stabilized austenitic stainless steels, (*e*) steels with low carbon content, and (*f*) steels that are particularly machinable.

This classification is, however, complicated by overlapping effects. For example, a lower carbon content to reduce sensitization also reduces susceptibility to work hardening. And it is also confused by the fact that the

Table 4.5. Suggested Stress-Relieving Treatments for Austenitic Stainless Steels

Anticipated service environment, or other reason for treatment	Suggested thermal treatment* (entered in order of decreasing preference)		
	Extra-low-carbon grades, such as 304L and 316L	Stabilized grades, such as 318, 321, and 347	Unstabilized grades, such as 304 and 316
Severe stress corrosion	A, B	B, A	(a)
Moderate stress corrosion	A, B, C	B, A, C	C(a)
Mild stress corrosion	A, B, C, E, F	B, A, C, E, F	C, F
Remove peak stresses only	F	F	F
No stress corrosion	None required	None required	None required
Intergranular corrosion	A, C(b)	A, C, B(b)	C
Stress relief after severe forming	A, C	A, C	C
Relief between forming operations	A, B, C	B, A, C	C(c)
Structural soundness(d)	A, C, B	A, C, B	C
Dimensional stability	G	G	G

*Key to letter designations of treatments:

A—Anneal at 1950 to 2050 F; slow cool. E—Stress relieve at 900 to 1200 F; slow cool.
B—Stress relieve at 1650 F; slow cool. F—Stress relieve at below 900 F; slow cool.
C—Anneal at 1950 to 2050 F; quench(e) G—Stress relieve at 400 to 900 F; slow cool.
D—Stress relieve at 1650 F; quench(e) (Usual time, 4 hr per inch of section.)

(a) To allow the optimum stress-relieving treatment, the use of stabilized or extra-low-carbon grades is recommended.
(b) In most instances, no heat treatment is required, but where fabrication procedures may have sensitized the stainless steel the heat treatments noted may be employed.
(c) Treatment A, B, or D also may be used, if followed by treatment C when forming is completed.
(d) Where severe fabricating stresses coupled with high service loading may cause cracking. Also, after welding heavy sections.
(e) Or cool rapidly.

chemistry permitted by AISI specifications may allow the low chemistry end of one grade to extend into the high chemistry end of another. Thus one *could* buy 301 and 302 of identical composition.

With these reservations in mind, we will describe the steels as we have itemized them above. Notch ductility values will not be itemized, however, because it is safe to make the generalization that notch ductility of the austenitic stainless steels is high at all temperatures down to liquid nitrogen temperatures (and probably lower), so long as two conditions are satisfied. First, the steel must not be sensitized. Second, if it has been cold worked to produce a martensitic phase, a lower notch ductility must be expected. Outside these restrictions, Izod impact values of about 100 ft-lb are usually obtained at temperatures of −320 F (liquid nitrogen). Data at lower temperatures are scarce, but those available show continued good impact properties.

Basic 18–8 Steels: AISI 301, 302, and 304. These steels account for more than half of austenitic stainless steel production. Table 4.4 shows

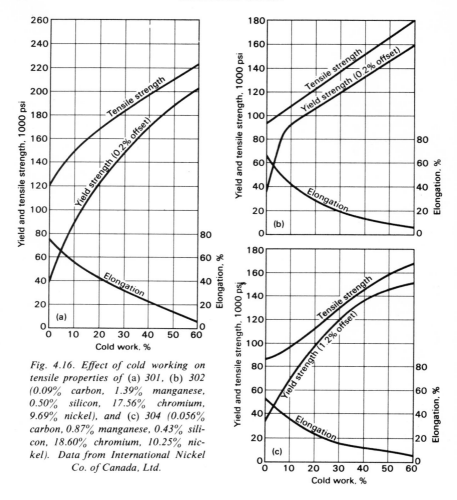

Fig. 4.16. Effect of cold working on tensile properties of (a) 301, (b) 302 (0.09% carbon, 1.39% manganese, 0.50% silicon, 17.56% chromium, 9.69% nickel), and (c) 304 (0.056% carbon, 0.87% manganese, 0.43% silicon, 18.60% chromium, 10.25% nickel). Data from International Nickel Co. of Canada, Ltd.

the effect of cold working; a more detailed analysis is shown in Fig. 4.16. That the pronounced work hardening is associated with the formation of a "martensitic" phase is indicated in Table 4.6: the lower Izod values may not be conclusive, but the "magnetic pull" must be related to the production of a substantially body-centered cubic phase produced by a shear process. Anyway, you can perform the experiment yourself. 302 in the annealed condition is not magnetic. Hammer it, when it is cold, and it will be noticeably attracted to a magnet. Just *how* cold it must be if the effect is to be appreciably developed and just how much cold working is needed depend upon the precise composition of the alloy.

Table 4.6. Effect of Low-Temperature Straining on 18-8 Stainless Steel(a)

Strain, %	Temp of straining, F	Hardness, Bhn	Izod value(b), ft-lb	Magnetic pull
0	80	140	90	0
	-110	140	90	0
	-320	140	90	0
12	80	200	80	0
	-110	285	45	85
	-320	310	35	100
20	80	220	75	0
	-110	350	25	(c)
	-320	390	15	(c)

(a) Data from S. L. Hoyt, *Metal Data*, Reinhold Publishing Corp., New York, 1952
(b) Tested at -295 F
(c) Straining had a marked effect.

301, which has a lower chromium range and, what is more to the point, a lower nickel content (see Table 4.4), is more susceptible than 302 to cold work. This is indicated in Fig. 4.16. The austenite is less stable in 301.

At this point it is fair to offer a warning: the austenitic stainless steels are properly recommended for subzero applications. However, if the alloy is cold worked at a subzero temperature, then its notch ductility is reduced, as Table 4.6 has shown. The reduction becomes more marked as the nickel content is decreased.

304 contains a maximum of 0.08% carbon, and the chromium range is increased by 1 or 2% (which may not show in the particular shipment). However, the lower carbon reduces susceptibility to sensitization (although a more complete remedy must lie in the selection of an extra-low-carbon or a stabilized grade) and also reduces the extent of work hardening, particularly at moderate amounts of cold work (see Fig. 4.16).

Creep properties of 304 have been compared with those of other stainless steels in Fig. 4.7.

Higher-Nickel Steel: AISI 305. To offset the work-hardening propensity, nickel can be increased beyond the normal range. 305 contains (as Table 4.4 shows) 10 to 13% nickel. The alloy is therefore used where an austenitic type is required, but where work hardening must be minimized. (It is, perhaps, in this context that a ferritic grade might be considered.) The effect is most marked at lower amounts of cold work.

Especially Corrosion-Resistant Steels: AISI 302B, 309, 310, 314, 316, and 317. Additional corrosion resistance can be given by increasing the alloy contents of the steels, which also increases the cost, of course. Table 4.4 indicates the range of compositions of these alloys. 302B and 314 are modifications of 302 and 310, respectively, through the addition of silicon: 302B contains, instead of the usual 1% maximum, 2 to 3%, and 314 contains between 1.5 and 3%. The main purpose of the addition is to reduce the rate of carburization and oxidation at elevated temperatures. Mechanical properties are similar to those of the types from which the higher-silicon alloys are derived.

It will be noted that 310 may contain up to 0.25% carbon: at a high level it would work harden appreciably. But for a given carbon level the chromium-nickel balance is maintained to give similar mechanical properties in the worked condition to 304.

Perhaps the most familiar method of improving corrosion resistance or, at any rate, of increasing the range of environments in which the austenitic steels give good service, is through the addition of molybdenum. And because molybdenum is a ferritizer, the nickel content of 316 and 317 is increased to ensure austenitic stability. With 2% molybdenum in 316 and 4% in 317 the resistance to pitting in chloride solutions is improved. (This matter is dealt with more completely in Chapter 8.)

Increased chromium content brings with it a greater possibility of the formation of the sigma phase; a higher carbon content, while it induces a greater susceptibility to sensitization, is offset to some extent by an increased chromium addition.

Creep properties of these steels and other stainless steels have been compared in Fig. 4.7.

Stabilized Steels: AISI 321, 347, and 348. Sensitization can be reduced by the addition of strong carbide formers to the basic stainless steel composition. The composition of 321 is similar to 304, but titanium is added to a minimum of five times the carbon content. In 347 the carbide former is a mixture of columbium and tantalum added to the extent of (minimally) ten times the carbon content. In 348 the same composition pertains, but a maximum of 0.1% tantalum is permitted: this type is, therefore, essentially columbium-stabilized. The room-temperature mechanical properties of the stabilized grades are similar to those of 304. Differences arise, of course, in corrosion performance and, as we will see, in some aspects of fabricability. High-temperature properties of the stabilized grades show improved resistance to creep and rupture over 304.

Extra-Low-Carbon Steels. 304 and 316 are available with a maximum carbon content of 0.03% (compared with their normal value of 0.08% maximum). At this low carbon level they are designated by the letter "L" after the type number: 304L, 316L. Low-carbon 309 and 310 are designated 309S and 310S. The purpose is, of course, to reduce sensitization; mechanical properties are very similar to the normal-carbon grades.

Machinable Steels: AISI 303 and 303Se. Additions of sulfur, selenium, and phosphorus can be made to the 302 composition to improve machinability. The only mechanical property that suffers a little is notch ductility:

values are a little lower, and the spread is much greater in the machinable grade, compared with 302.

Manganese-Substituted Austenitic Stainless Steels

The 200 series of stainless steels was developed in the early 1930's and came into use during the Korean war to conserve nickel. About 4% nickel is replaced by 7% manganese and 0.25% (maximum) nitrogen. The compositions and mechanical properties of 201 and 202, standard AISI types, are given in Table 4.4 and can be compared with the compositions and properties of the equivalent 300 grades, 301 and 302.

It has been suggested that use of the 200 series is still limited because they were introduced as a substitute and are therefore considered to be in some way substandard. Price, on a straight weight basis, is roughly the same as that of the corresponding 300-series steels, but this comparison is hardly a fair one. Steels of the 200 series have yield strengths about 40% higher than the corresponding 300 series and the density is about 3% less. The higher yield strength pertains to both annealed and cold worked materials, and the ductility (measured by elongation in simple tension) remains as high as, or is higher than, that of the corresponding 300-series steel.

Notch ductility, measured by the Izod impact test, is typical of austenitic materials; that is, there is no transition temperature.

Table 4.7. Stress-Rupture Properties of 200-Series Stainless Steels(a)

AISI	Temp, F	Rupture strength, psi			Elong in 2 in., %	
		100-hr	1000-hr	10,000-hr(b)	100-hr	1000-hr
201	1200	29,000	22,000	16,500	14.0	14.0
	1350	15,000	10,000	6,600	16.5	22.0
	1500	7,400	4,000	....	35.0	42.0
202	1200	31,000	25,000	20,000	32.5	23.0
	1350	16,200	11,100	7,600	44.0	39.0
	1500	8,800	4,400	....	45.0	42.0
204(c)	1200	30,000	23,600	18,000	9.5	10.0
	1350	17,500	11,200	7,200	25.0	33.5
	1500	8,800	4,400	....	45.0	42.0
204L(d)	1200	29,000	20,300	14,200	22.0	9.0
	1350	11,000	6,700	4,100	16.0	15.0
	1500	5,000	2,600	....	18.5	....

(a) Data from Union Carbide Corp.
(b) Extrapolated values
(c) The composition of 204, which is not officially recognized as an AISI type number, is as follows: 17.0–19.0% Cr, 4.0–6.0% Ni, 7.5–10.0% Mn, 0.25% max N, 0.08% max C, 1.00% max Si, 0.045% max P, 0.03% max S.
(d) The composition of 204L, which is not officially recognized as an AISI type number, is the same as that of 204 except for 5.0–7.0% Ni and 0.03% max C.

High-temperature mechanical properties are given in Table 4.7, and reflect greater strengths than the corresponding 300 types. For example, the rupture strength of 202 at 1200 F is higher than that of 302, and even of 316 (see Fig. 4.7). However, at temperatures above 1550 F resistance to scaling in oxidizing atmospheres is lower.

Corrosion resistance is more fully dealt with in Chapter 8. Here, to complete the comparison with 300-series steels, we will simply state that experience to date shows comparable or better resistance in most corrosive mediums. It seems only reasonable to add, however, that because of the limited use of the 200 series (they represent only about 5% of the austenitic stainless steel consumption), corrosion data are not as comprehensive as for the more familiar 300 grades.

The 200 series is not produced in stabilized grades, although extra-low-carbon grades are available. The problem of sensitization, then, is still with us, but it is claimed that for a given carbon content the 200-series alloys are less susceptible than the 300 series. We wish to qualify this contention by pointing out that while we do not doubt the claim, the available amount of data is limited.

Precipitation-Hardening Stainless Steels

We have seen that high strength in stainless steels can be developed by conventional heat treatments in the martensitic class and by cold working in the ferritic and—more pertinently—austenitic classes. The strengthening mechanisms carry with them the counterbalancing disadvantage of a reduced ductility and notch ductility—the perpetual metallurgical problem, of course. Further, cold worked stainless steels and the quenched-and-tempered martensitic steels are less corrosion-resistant than the annealed materials.

More exasperating is the fact that at high strength levels fabrication becomes more difficult and, at times, impossible. If high strength is required of an austenitic stainless, then, unless the forming process offers just that amount of cold work that gives us the mechanical properties we seek, it may be quite impossible to integrate cold working for strength with the necessary fabrication process: the component cannot usually be cold worked *after* fabrication, and it may be difficult or impossible to make the component from cold worked stock.

The precipitation-hardening stainless steels offer an alternative means of obtaining high strength in a stainless material. Corrosion resistance for a given strength level is usually superior (but field data are not yet substantial), and while ductility is much the same as it is in the corresponding non-precipitation-hardening grade at the same strength level (if such a strength is attainable in the ordinary grade), fabrication is easier—because the strengthening process is conducted *after* fabrication by the simple means of *aging* at a temperature around 1000 F.

The precipitation-hardening class can be divided into three groups: (*a*) martensitic, (*b*) semi-austenitic, and (*c*) austenitic. Although the austenitic grades have not yet received an AISI number, most of the steels in the other groups are incorporated in the AISI high-temperature, high-strength classification (designated by a three-digit number in the 600 series). However, most of the precipitation-hardening grades are better known by the trade designations of their manufacturers. Table 4.8 gives nominal compositions and mechanical properties of the precipitation-hardening steels.

Martensitic Steels: AISI 630 and 635. The first commercially available steel of the precipitation-hardening class, "Stainless W" (635), was put on the market in 1946. The other commercial member of the martensitic group is "17-4 PH" (630). These two steels have a basically similar low-carbon martensitic stainless composition (about 16% chromium, 0.05% carbon), but the elements that induce precipitation strengthening are different. This, however, need not concern us.

The as-quenched hardness of these steels is much lower than that of martensitic 410 stainless because of the substantially lower carbon content, and they are readily workable in this condition. Equally, of course, they have not developed the strength and hardness we expect in a martensitic grade.

Subsequent heat treatment involves *aging*, to permit the formation of the *preprecipitate* that has been described in Chapter 3. Developed properties of 17-4 PH are given in Table 4.8. For a given strength, room-temperature ductility is much the same as that of 414 and 431. Further, Izod data at subzero temperatures show a transition at about room temperature, but at no temperature are the values high—they are similar, in fact, to those of a martensitic stainless steel of similar strength.

We can summarize the room-temperature and subzero properties in this way, then:

1. The use of a precipitation-hardening grade can permit us to attain a higher yield strength than that obtainable in the conventional martensitic grades.

2. At the high strength level, ductility and notch ductility are low. Therefore, design should accommodate this deficiency, and further, tests to supplement the Izod data should be performed to evaluate the performance of the component.

3. Because of the lower carbon content and the fact that properties do not depend upon precipitated carbide, corrosion resistance is better than in the conventional martensitic grades.

4. Because of the ductility of the material after solution treating and

Table 4.8. Nominal Compositions and Room-Temperature

AISI type	Trade desig-nation	Composition(b), %	Condition
Martensitic			
630	17–4 PH	0.04 C, 0.25 Mn, 0.20 P, 0.010 S, 0.60 Si, 16.0 Cr, 4.0 Ni, (3.2 Cu, 0.25 Cb + Ta)	Solution annealed Aged 900 F, 1 hr, AC Aged 925 F, 4 hr, AC Aged 1100 F, 4 hr, AC
Semi-Austenitic			
631	17–7 PH (sheet)	0.07 C, 0.60 Mn, 0.020 P, 0.010 S, 0.40 Si, 17.0 Cr, 7.0 Ni, (1.15 Al)	Solution annealed Aged 1050 F Aged 950 F after refrigeration Aged 900 F after cold rolling
632	PH 15–7 Mo (sheet)	0.07 C, 0.60 Mn, 0.020 P, 0.010 S, 0.40 Si, 15.0 Cr, 7.0 Ni, 2.20 Mo, (1.15 Al)	Solution annealed Aged 1050 F Aged 950 F after refrigeration Aged 900 F after cold rolling
633	AM-350 (sheet)	0.10 C, 0.80 Mn, 0.020 P, 0.010 S, 0.25 Si, 16.5 Cr, 4.3 Ni, (2.75 Mo, 0.10 N)	Solution annealed Double aged Subzero cooled and aged Cold rolled and tempered(c)
634	AM–355 (bar, cold rolled sheet)	0.13 C, 0.95 Mn, 0.020 P, 0.010 S, 0.25 Si, 15.5 Cr, 4.3 Ni, (2.75 Mo, 0.10 N)	Solution annealed Double aged Subzero cooled and aged Cold rolled and tempered(c)
Austenitic			
· · ·	17–10 P	0.12 C, 0.75 Mn, (0.25 P), 0.030 S, 0.60 Si, 17.0 Cr, 10.0 Ni	Solution annealed 2050 F, $\frac{1}{2}$ hr, WQ Aged 1300 F, 24 hr Aged 1300 + 1200 F, 12 + 24 hr
· · ·	17–14 CuMo	0.12 C, 0.75 Mn, 0.020 P, 0.010 S, 0.50 Si, 16.0 Cr, 14.0 Ni, (3.0 Cu, 2.5 Mo, 0.50 Cb, 0.25 Ti)	Solution annealed 2250 F, $\frac{1}{2}$ hr, WQ, and aged 1350 F, 5 hr

(a) Data from International Nickel Co. of Canada, Ltd.
(b) Elements in parentheses are responsible for properties developed by heat treatment.

Mechanical Properties of Precipitation-Hardening Stainless Steels(a)

0.2% Offset yield strength, 1000 psi	Tensile strength, 1000 psi	Elong in 2 in., %	Reduction of area, %	Hardness		Impact data, ft-lb	AISI type
				Bhn	Rockwell		
110	150	12	45	363	....	....	630
185	200	14	50	420	C44	20 (Izod)	
175	190	14	54	409	C42	25 (Izod)	
135	150	17	58	332	C34	45 (Izod)	
40	130	35	....	...	B85	....	631
190	205	9	....	...	C43	....	
210	225	6	....	...	C47	....	
260	265	2	....	...	C49	....	
55	130	35	....	...	B88	....	632
205	215	7	....	...	C44	....	
215	235	6	....	...	C48	....	
260	265	2	....	...	C49	....	
60	145	40	....	...	C20	....	633
149	186	12.5	....	...	C41.5	....	
173	206	13.5	....	...	C45	14 (Charpy)	
190	210	10	....	...	....	....	
57	160	26	....	...	....	....	634
153	188	16.5	51.7	...	....	....	
182	216	19	38.5	...	....	17 (Charpy)	
210	230	12	....	...	....	....	
38	89	70	76	...	C10(d)	117–120 (Izod)	...
88	137	25	39	...	C30	39–42 (Izod)	
98	144	20	32	...	C32	33–40 (Izod)	
42	86	45	63	...	....	....	...

(c) "Tempered" is used here instead of "aged" because the material is not initially in a fully solution annealed condition.

(d) Estimated value

quenching and because of the subsequent strengthening during aging, fabrication (forming, machining) is facilitated.

If the precipitation-hardening martensitic stainless is heated much above its aging temperature, overaging occurs: the steel softens. This permits it to be more easily worked; equally, it restricts the maximum safe operating temperature of the material. If the steel is overaged, full strength can be regained only by resoaking, quenching and properly aging.

Creep-rupture properties of 17–4 PH are summarized in Table 4.9. For long-term use, temperatures are usually restricted to below 900 F.

Table 4.9. Creep-Rupture Properties of 17–4 PH (Aged at 900 F)(a)

Temp, F	Ultimate stress, psi		Elong in 2 in., %		Reduction of area, %		Stress to produce a creep rate of 0.1% in 1000 hr, psi	Stress to produce a creep rate of 0.01% in 1000 hr, psi
	100-hr	1000-hr	100-hr	1000-hr	100-hr	1000-hr		
600	164,000	158,000	3	2	7	6	135,000	125,000
700	156,000	150,000	3	2	7	6	105,000	100,000
800	140,000	128,000	4	4	8	6	60,000	43,000
900	95,000	60,000	5	12	9	25	23,000	....

(a) Data from Republic Steel Corp.

Semi-Austenitic Steels: AISI 631, 632, 633, and 634. The distinction between these steels and the previous group is that quenching to room temperature after soaking produces an austenitic (not a martensitic) structure. However, martensite is eventually formed by one of two processes. The first, and more easily understood, involves cooling the steel to a subzero temperature, at which martensite forms. The second involves a heat treatment that, through the precipitation of complexes that contain chromium and carbon, depletes the matrix material in those elements. Now, the temperature at which martensite forms in the matrix depends upon the composition of the matrix, and, at the depleted chromium and carbon levels, martensite now forms during cooling to room temperature. In both cases full strength is obtained by subsequent aging.

Hence two types of heat treatment and fabrication emerge, and both are generally applicable to any of the four steels in this group. They are:

1. Hold at 1750 F, cool to room temperature. Fabricate. Subzero quench to −100 F, hold for 3 to 8 hr. Age between 850 and 1050 F.

2. Hold at about 1400 F for 1 to 3 hr, cool to room temperature. Fabricate. Age between 850 and 1050 F. (This is known as *double aging*.)

Specific heat treatments are best obtained from manufacturers' data, but it is fair to generalize with the comment that the first type of heat treatment is more satisfactory for severely deformed parts—the room-temperature properties prior to fabrication and aging show a greater ductility.

A final variation depends upon the effects of cold working superposed upon the aging process. The material is available in the cold rolled condition (from the manufacturer), and subsequent treatment involves only aging. However, the ductility is lower in the cold rolled condition and forming processes are therefore limited.

Creep-rupture properties of 17–7 PH and PH 15–7 Mo are given in Table 4.10.

Austenitic Steels. These steels retain their austenitic structure at all temperatures. The development of properties simply involves the precipitation process occurring in the austenite matrix. This is effected by an initial solution treatment at about 2050 F followed by quenching to room

Table 4.10. Creep-Rupture Properties of 17–7 PH and PH 15–7 Mo Sheet, Strip, and Plate(a)

Steel	Temp, F	Condition(b)	Stress to rupture, psi		Stress to produce 0.1% permanent deformation in 1000 hr, psi	Stress to produce 0.2% permanent deformation in 1000 hr, psi
			100-hr	1000-hr		
17–7 PH	600	RH 950	188,000	180,000	105,000	126,000
		TH 1050	170,000	158,000	87,000	105,000
		CH 900	220,000	216,000	....	....
	700	RH 950	169,000	146,000	60,000	87,000
		TH 1050	130,000	122,000	57,000	70,000
		CH 900	194,000	180,000	....	....
	800	RH 950	113,000	92,000	31,000	36,000
		TH 1050	110,000	90,000	40,000	45,000
		CH 900	135,000	73,000	....	....
	900	RH 950	61,000	44,000	12,500	14,000
		TH 1050	78,000	52,000	15,000	18,000
		CH 900	53,000	36,000	....	....
PH 15–7 Mo	600	RH 950	202,000	200,000	130,000	150,000
	700	RH 950	193,000	191,000	120,000	143,000
	800	RH 950	174,000	171,000	95,000	108,000
	900	RH 950	125,000	108,000	40,000	44,000

(a) Data from Republic Steel Corp.
(b) Code is as follows: RH 950 represents aged at 950 F after refrigeration; TH 1050 represents aged at 1050 F, CH 900 represents aged at 900 F after cold rolling.

temperature and aging at about 1300 F. Fabrication follows the quenching procedure. Table 4.8 shows that room-temperature strength levels do not reach the high values attained in the martensitic and semi-martensitic precipitation-hardening steels. For this reason, presumably, the AISI has not included them in the high-strength high-temperature designations.

Because of the higher aging temperature, the austenitic steels of this class can be used at higher temperatures than the other two classes. Low-temperature notch ductility, as reflected by impact tests, is generally poorer than in the ordinary austenitic grades.

Corrosion resistance of these alloys is difficult to specify. 17–14 CuMo is said to have a better corrosion resistance than 316. However, information about the performance of the alloys is sparse.

Stainless-Clad Steels

Over-all properties of stainless-clad steels are difficult to summarize because of the large range of possible combinations of cladding and backing steels. The most common grades are specified under ASTM A263 and A264, and tests to evaluate the strength of the bond are included among the requirements.

The difference between the thermal-expansion coefficients of a mild steel backing and austenitic cladding should be borne in mind when a clad material is assessed for high- or fluctuating-temperature service. Calculations of stresses arising through different thermal-expansion coefficients are seemingly impossible to make, because it is difficult to assess the residual stresses residing in the material in the cold, as-received condition. If the problem is thought to be significant—depending upon service conditions—an evaluation should be made by experimental tests.

Chapter 5

Cast Stainless Steels

Cast stainless steels, like wrought stainless steels, can be categorized as martensitic, ferritic, austenitic, or precipitation-hardening. However, the composition specifications laid down by AISI for wrought stainless steels are not followed in the cast materials. It is true that many cast stainless steels do conform to composition requirements that correspond roughly

Table 5.1. Designations and Compositions of Corrosion-Resistant Stainless Steel Castings

ACI type (a)	Wrought type (AISI)(b)	Composition, %					
		C (max)	Mn (max)	Si (max)	Cr	Ni	Other(c)
CA-15	410	0.15	1.00	1.50	11.5–14	1 max	0.5 max Mo(d)
CA-40	420	0.40	1.00	1.50	11.5–14	1 max	0.5 max Mo(d)
CB-30	431	0.30	1.00	1.00	18–22	2 max	· · · ·
CC-50	446	0.50	1.00	1.00	26–30	4 max	· · · ·
CD-4MCu	· · ·	0.04	1.00	1.00	25–27	4.75–6.00	2.75–3.25 Cu
CE-30	· · ·	0.30	1.50	2.00	26–30	8–11	· · · ·
CF-3	304L	0.03	1.50	2.00	18–21	8–11	· · · ·
CF-3M	316L	0.03	1.50	1.50	18–21	9–12	2.0–3.0 Mo
CF-8	304	0.08	1.50	2.00	18–21	8–11	· · · ·
CF-20	302	0.20	1.50	2.00	18–21	8–11	· · · ·
CF-8M	316	0.08	1.50	1.50	18–21	9–12	2.0–3.0 Mo
CF-12M	316	0.12	1.50	1.50	18–21	9–12	2.0–3.0 Mo
CF-8C	347	0.08	1.50	2.00	18–21	9–12	Cb(e)
CF-16F	303	0.16	1.50	2.00	18–21	9–12	Mo, Se(f)
CG-8M	317	0.08	1.50	1.50	18–21	8–11	3.00 min Mo
CH-20	309	0.20	1.50	2.00	22–26	12–15	· · · ·
CK-20	310	0.20	1.50	2.00	23–27	19–22	· · · ·
CN-7M	· · ·	0.07	1.50	(g)	18–22	21–31	Mo, Cu(g)

(a) Most of these standard grades are covered by ASTM A296-64T and A351-64.

(b) Type numbers of wrought alloys are listed only for nominal identification of corresponding wrought and cast grades. Composition ranges of the cast alloys are not the same as for the corresponding wrought alloys; cast alloy designations should be used for castings.

(c) Phosphorus is 0.04% max except in CF-16F, which has 0.17% max; sulfur is 0.04% max in all grades.

(d) Molybdenum not intentionally added.

(e) Cb, 8 × C min, 1.0% max; or Cb-Ta, 10 × C min, 1.35% max.

(f) Mo, 1.5% max; Se, 0.2 to 0.35%.

(g) Several proprietary alloy compositions within the stated chromium and nickel ranges contain varying amounts of silicon, molybdenum, and copper.

to an AISI designation, but the pertinent specification for cast materials of martensitic, ferritic, and austenitic stainless steels is that of either the Alloy Casting Institute (ACI) or the Society of Automotive Engineers. (There are also federal and military specifications, but we will not discuss them here.) The precipitation-hardening alloys maintain their trade designations; the manganese-substituted austenitic stainless steels are rarely used in cast form.

Stainless steel specifications of the ACI fall into two groups: corrosion-resistant steel castings and heat-resistant steel castings. The standard designations and composition ranges for the corrosion-resistant castings are given in Table 5.1: they have the prefix "C." The designations and compositions for the heat-resisting alloys are given in Table 5.2: they have the prefix "H." Table 4.1 (p. 29) has already attempted a correlation of specifications of ACI, AISI, SAE, and ASTM.

Tables 5.1 and 5.2 show the approximate AISI designations for wrought materials of similar composition to cast materials, and you will notice that, for example, a cast stainless corresponding roughly to 310 appears in Table 5.1 as CK-20, and in Table 5.2 as HK. And there are similarities between other entries in the two tables. In fact, it is difficult to make a clear separation. One reasonable criterion lies in the carbon content. Generally, the carbon content of a corrosion-resistant casting is lower than that of a heat-resisting alloy of otherwise similar composition.

Table 5.2. Designations and Compositions of Heat-Resistant Stainless Steel Castings

ACI type	Wrought type (AISI)(a)	ASTM specification(b)	Composition(c), %			
			C	Cr	Ni	Si (max)
HA	· · ·	A217-C12	0.20 max	8–10	· · · ·	1.00
HB	· · ·	· · · ·	0.30 max	18–22	2 max	2.00
HC	446	A297	0.50 max	26–30	4 max	2.00
HD	327	A297	0.50 max	26–30	4–7	2.00
HE	· · ·	A297	0.20–0.50	26–30	8–11	2.00
HF	302B	A297	0.20–0.40	19–23	9–12	2.00
HH	309	A297, A447	0.20–0.50	24–28	11–14	2.00
HI	· · ·	A297	0.20–0.50	26–30	14–18	2.00
HK	310	A297, A351	0.20–0.60	24–28	18–22	2.00
HL	· · ·	A297	0.20–0.60	28–32	18–22	2.00
HN	· · ·	A297	0.20–0.50	19–23	23–27	2.00
HT	330	A297, A448	0.35–0.75	13–17	33–37	2.50

(a) Type numbers of wrought alloys are listed only for nominal identification of corresponding wrought and cast grades. Cast alloy designations should be used for castings.

(b) Alloy designations are the same as ACI except for A217, A447 and A448.

(c) Manganese is 0.35 to 0.65% for HA, 1% for HC, 1.5% for HD, and 2% for the other alloys. Phosphorus and sulfur are 0.04% max. Molybdenum is not intentionally added except in HA, which has 0.90 to 1.20% Mo; maximum for other alloys is 0.5% Mo. HH also contains 0.2% N.

Nevertheless, it is a little frustrating, and one can seek solace in the fact that despite this additional set of specification numbers we can still make sense by associating stainless steels with their respective classes.

The alloys of Table 5.1 include stainless steels that are heat treatable. The first four alloys listed, all in the 400 series, can be air or oil hardened by cooling from about 1800 F. They are usually tempered between 1000 and 1400 F; below this temperature range they become embrittled. CD-4MCu is ferritic and can be precipitation hardened. The remainder of the alloys in Table 5.1 are austenitic.

The alloys of Table 5.2 include no heat treatable castings (the heat treatable compositions are not those with best heat-resisting properties), with the exception of the first in the list, HA. The next two steels, HB and HC, are ferritic; the remainder are austenitic. Thus most of the stainless steel castings produced are of austenitic composition.

The austenitic alloys used for corrosion-resistant service (Table 5.1) are

Table 5.3. Room-Temperature Mechanical Properties of Corrosion-Resistant Alloy Castings(a)

ACI type	Heat treatment	Tensile strength, psi	0.2% Offset yield strength, psi	Elong in 2 in., %	Hardness, Bhn	Charpy impact (keyhole notch), ft-lb
CD-4MCu	2050 F, furnace cool to 1750 F, WQ	95,000	70,000	25	230	...
CE-30	As-cast	95,000	60,000	15	170	...
	1950–2050 F, WQ	97,000	63,000	18	170	...
CF-3	As-cast	81,000	38,000	53	...	...
CF-8	1950–2050 F, WQ	77,000	37,000	55	140	74
CF-20	2000+ F, WQ	77,000	36,000	50	163	60
CF-3M	As-cast	83,000	40,000	50	...	...
CF-8M	1950–2100 F, WQ	80,000	42,000	50	156–170	70
CF-12M	2000+ F, WQ	80,000	42,000	50	156–170	70
CF-8C	1950–2050 F, WQ	77,000	38,000	39	149	30
CF-16F	2000+ F, WQ	77,000	40,000	52	150	75
CG-8M	As-cast	83,000	40,000	50	...	...
CH-20	2000+ F, WQ	88,000	50,000	38	190	30
CK-20	2100 F, WQ	76,000	38,000	37	144	50(b)
CN-7M	1950–2050 F, WQ	69,000	32,000	48	130	70

(a) Data from International Nickel Co. of Canada, Ltd. (b) Izod V-notch data.

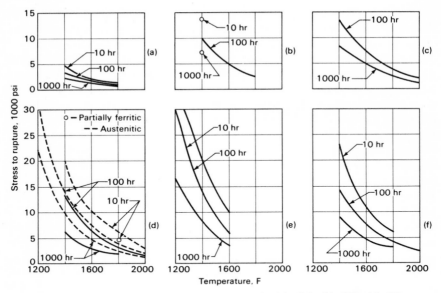

Fig. 5.1. Stress to rupture versus temperature for (a) *HC,* (b) *HD,* (c) *HI,* (d) *HH,* (e) *HF, and* (f) *HK*

generally annealed—heated to about 2000 F and quenched—to ensure that the carbides are in solution and that corrosion resistance is maximal. The austenitic alloys used for heat-resisting purposes (Table 5.2) are generally used in the as-cast condition. The carbon content (usually high, for the sake of mechanical strength at temperature) will lead to carbide precipitation at service temperature, anyway.

Austenitic alloys may contain some ferrite. This subject will be discussed (Chapter 6) in connection with fusion welding where, of course, the weld bead is simply a small casting. The Schaeffler diagram (Fig. 6.5, p 88) offers a means of calculating whether a casting will, despite its "austenitic" composition, contain ferrite. The presence of ferrite reduces corrosion resistance, and usually notch ductility, but increases strength.

Room-temperature mechanical properties of the corrosion-resistant series are shown in Table 5.3. Elevated-temperature properties of selected heat-resistant alloys are shown in Fig. 5.1. Machining and welding practices depend upon the same considerations that pertain to the wrought steels and are described in Chapter 6.

Chapter 6

Fabrication of Stainless Steels

Fabrication includes all processes whereby a casting or a mill product is developed into a shape suitable for incorporation into a finished article, and the assembly of the article or structure. Usually, the primary operations of casting and hot rolling to produce sections and flat products are not included under fabrication. In other words, it is assumed that the fabricator receives a raw shape, which he fabricates into a finished product. In any case, a description of stainless steel foundry practice and the operations of rolling mills falls outside the scope of this book.

The principal types of stainless steel fabrication are forming, cutting, joining, machining, and finishing, and these processes will be discussed in relation to the common stainless steels. The comparatively recent introduction of powder-metallurgy stainless parts seems to us, however, to warrant a brief treatment; therefore a short section on this subject is included at the end of the chapter.

Cold Forming

Most of the cold forming operations are performed on sheet, although *chipless machining* methods of pressing, swaging, etc., are becoming increasingly popular. Cold forming operations on sheet include (*a*) bending, by brake press, rolls, or the process of stretch bending; (*b*) roll forming; (*c*) spinning; (*d*) drawing. In stretch bending, sheet is held at each end and pulled while it is bent over a radius. Spinning is a process in which a rotating sheet of metal is drawn over a die by a free-rolling tool. In *manual spinning* there is little change in the thickness of the metal; in *compression spinning* or *flow turning* stretching occurs and the sheet becomes thinned. Highly polished dies and tools are used during forming to reduce metal pickup, and thorough cleaning between forming and subsequent annealing is vital if local carburization and a consequent lowering of corrosion resistance is to be avoided. Grain size for optimum formability is medium to fine (ASTM grain size number 5 to 8).

Springback. In any bending operation that produces a permanent deformation of the piece, some metal on either side of the neutral axis (Fig. 6.1) suffers compressive or tensile plastic deformation. On either

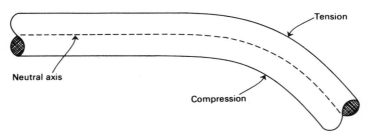

Fig. 6.1. Stresses in bending

side of the neutral axis, elastic stresses remain in those parts of the material that have passed the elastic limit and those, of course, that lie nearer the neutral axis and have not reached the elastic limit. And we must not forget that the actual values of yield strength, ultimate tensile strength and ductility change as a result of the cold working suffered by the steel—this is even more important when we come to consider the austenitic steels. The residual elastic stresses cause *springback*—the tendency of a deformed piece of sheet to return part way to its original shape. In a qualitative way, we might deduce that the amount of springback would increase as (*a*) the elastic limit of the material increases, (*b*) the plastic strain increases (because this increases the amount of deformed material in the piece), (*c*) the cold working effect increases (this raises the elastic limit), and (*d*) the elastic modulus decreases. For a given material we can assume that (*d*) is negligible—although, as a matter of precise fact, it may change because of effects of preferred orientation. But this need not concern us here.

The amount of plastic strain involved depends upon both the thickness of the piece and the radius of the bend. It does not depend upon the total bend angle. Thus the amount of springback per degree of bend increases as the ratio of bend radius to sheet thickness increases, and there will be less springback in a given piece of sheet when it is bent through a small radius than when it is bent through a large radius.

Calculations of springback are difficult and the amount of springback depends upon the method of bending employed. For example, stretch bending produces a stress gradient across the section that is nearly uniform, and hence springback is reduced. On the other hand, in compression spinning, in which metal is pressed and stretched out by a roller against a rotating form block, high tensile stresses are developed at the outer radius while the inner radius is in compression. Thus springback is pronounced. Table 6.1 gives approximate amounts of springback for 201, 301, and 304 with varying amounts of cold work and different bend radii and thickness.

Table 6.1. Approximate Springback in Stainless Steel Parts

Alloy	Part thickness, in.	Desired part radius, in.	Desired part angle, deg	Spring-back angle, deg	Required form-block angle, deg	Radius of as-bent part, in.	Required form-block radius, in.
			Annealed Condition				
201	0.75	23.1	78.0	12	90	20.0	19.625
	0.625	10.0	60.0	5.76	65.76	9.12	8.81
301	0.75	23.1	78.0	9.43	87.43	20.6	20.225
	0.625	10.0	60.0	4.86	64.86	9.225	8.913
430	0.75	23.1	78.0	8.19	86.19	20.9	20.525
	0.625	10.0	60.0	3.3	63.3	9.48	9.167
			10% Cold Worked Condition				
201	0.75	23.1	78.0	21.9	91.9	18.0	17.625
	0.625	10.0	60.0	8.7	68.7	8.72	8.41
301	0.75	23.1	78.0	18.72	96.72	18.65	18.27
	0.625	10.0	60.0	8.40	68.4	8.775	8.46
430	0.75	23.1	78.0	10.92	88.92	20.31	19.935
	0.625	10.0	60.0	4.8	64.8	9.92	9.608

Ferritic Stainless Steel Sheet. The mechanical properties of ferritic stainless steels compared with those of low-carbon steels give the clue to the differences in cold forming methods for these materials. The higher yield strength of stainless implies that more power must be supplied to the forming equipment for a given amount of deformation; the higher ultimate tensile strength indicates that a higher load can be applied before rupture; the lower ductility measured in simple tension suggests less plastic deformation prior to fracture. Because ferritic stainless steels have a poor notch ductility at room temperature, the speed of application of the load in cold forming may be lower than that customarily used for a plain low-carbon steel, and warming the sheet to about 300 F may reduce a tendency to fracture.

As cold working proceeds, the yield strength increases and approaches the value of the ultimate tensile strength of the material. While this phenomenon is common to all metals that are worked below their recrystallization temperature, the rate of convergence of yield and ultimate is much more rapid in the ferritic stainless steels than in the austenitic grades. Since the yield point must be exceeded for plastic deformation, and hence for cold forming to occur, the close convergence of yield and ultimate tensile strengths is conducive to rupture. This and the rapid drop in ductility with cold working usually necessitate the use of fully annealed sheet and dictate intermediate annealing, so that after maximum tolerable work hardening the metal is once again put into its fully soft condition.

Ferritic grades respond to spinning in much the same way as they do to roll forming: the drop in ductility to very low values may call for more intermediate annealing stages than is customary with a low-carbon steel. This particularly applies to the higher-chromium grades of the class. In all drawing processes the low-ductility characteristics must, again, be accommodated, particularly in the high-chromium grades.

Austenitic Stainless Steel Sheet. Austenitic steels work harden as a result of a martensitic transformation, to an extent that depends upon chemical composition. The nickel content is particularly critical, and thus we find that 301 (6 to 8% nickel) work hardens the most, and 305 (10 to 13% nickel) hardens the least. Other grades are generally intermediate.

Associated with 305's lower tendency to work harden is its characteristic of showing a much more pronounced convergence of yield and ultimate tensile strengths than the other austenitic grades do. Thus, while its lower yield point would necessitate less deforming load for a given operation, the total amount of deformation prior to fracture is less: the thickness reduction is not so effectively countered by a higher developed strength in the location of thinning.

A compromise between reasonable work hardening and a satisfactory spread between yield and ultimate is found in 302, which is a popular grade for cold forming. However, the total permissible deformation prior to annealing is greatest in 301.

The cold forming operations applicable to austenitic stainless steels are the same as those applicable to ferritic stainless steels. However, the forming conditions differ. The austenitic steels are capable of greater deformation than the ferritic grades are, and thus a greater amount of reduction in a given single operation can be tolerated. Among the austenitic steels, a greater single reduction can be withstood in the most rapidly work-hardening steels (for example, 301) than in a grade such as 305, which work hardens less. The formability of cold worked austenitic steels is adequate to permit cold forming operations without prior annealing. However, during a sequence of forming operations, the extent of work hardening may necessitate intermediate annealing. Tables 6.2 and 6.3 show a comparison of cold bending characteristics of common 300-series steels in the annealed condition and in various tempered conditions. The better formability of austenitic steels is particularly apparent in such processes as stretch bending (where they will sustain a greater tensile deformation) and in severe drawing operations where high ductility is called for. However, because of the generally higher annealed strengths and the increase in strength in austenitic steels during cold working,

Table 6.2. Cold Bending Data for Annealed Plate, Sheet, and Strip(a,b)

Type	Gage, in.	Free bend	Controlled V-block bend
300 series	To 0.249	$180° \ R = \frac{1}{2}T$	$135° \ R = \frac{1}{2}T$
	0.250–0.500	$90° \ R = \frac{1}{2}T$	$135° \ R = T$
405, 410, 430	To 0.374	$180° \ R = T$	$135° \ R = T$
	0.375–0.500	$180° \ R = T$	$135° \ R = 2T$
442, 446	To 0.374	$180° \ R = T$	$135° \ R = T$
	0.375–0.500	$180° \ R = 2T$	$135° \ R = 2T$

(a) Data from Allegheny Ludlum Steel Corp.
(b) All bends are in the poor direction; that is, the axis of the bend is parallel to the direction of rolling. R is the radius of the bend; T is the thickness of the material.

Table 6.3. Cold Bending Data for 301, 302, and 316 in the Temper-Rolled Condition(a,b)

Type	Temper	Gage, in.	Free bend	Controlled V-block bend
301	$\frac{1}{4}$ hard	To 0.050	$180° \ R = \frac{1}{2}T$	$135° \ R = T$
		0.051–0.187	$90° \ R = T$	$135° \ R = 1\frac{1}{2}T$
	$\frac{1}{2}$ hard	To 0.050	$180° \ R = T$	$135° \ R = 2T$
		0.051–0.187	$90° \ R = T$	$135° \ R = 2T$
	$\frac{3}{4}$ hard	To 0.050	$180° \ R = 1\frac{1}{2}T$	$135° \ R = 3T$
		0.051–0.187	....	....
	Full hard	To 0.050	$180° \ R = 2T$	$135° \ R = 3T$
		0.051–0.187	....	....
302	$\frac{1}{4}$ hard	To 0.050	$180° \ R = \frac{1}{2}T$	$135° \ R = 2T$
		0.051–0.187	$90° \ R = T$	$135° \ R = 2T$
316	$\frac{1}{4}$ hard	To 0.050	$180° \ R = T$	$135° \ R = 2\frac{1}{2}T$
		0.051–0.187	$90° \ R = T$	$135° \ R = 3T$

(a) Data from Allegheny Ludlum Steel Corp.
(b) All bends are in the poor direction; that is, the axis of the bend is parallel to the direction of rolling. R is the radius of the bend; T is the thickness of the material.

greater working forces are required for the austenitic than for the ferritic steels.

The higher strength of the 200-series austenitic stainless steels calls for more power and leads to greater springback than in the equivalent 300 grades (Table 6.1). The slightly lower ductility and greater convergence of yield and ultimate lead one to the conclusion that 201 is less formable than 301. However, the difference in performance between the 300- and the corresponding 200-series steels is not great.

Precipitation-hardening austenitic stainless steels can be cold formed in the same way as the regular grades. The semi-austenitic precipitation-hardening steels should be fully solution treated prior to cold forming.

This involves annealing at about 1950 F, and sheet purchased from the mill is generally in this condition.

Stainless Steel Rod, Bar, and Wire. The principal cold forming processes for stainless steel rod, bar, and wire are cold heading, cold riveting, drawing, extrusion, and swaging.

Ferritic stainless steels behave similarly to plain low-carbon steels, with the exceptions caused by greater strength and lower ductility, which have been noted in an earlier section of this chapter. The machinable grades (416 and 430F) tend to split during cold heading or riveting, and during drawing they will tolerate only small drafts. Most severe deformation in cold heading is possible with 430.

Austenitic stainless steels work harden to a greater extent but will suffer more deformation prior to fracture (as we have already mentioned). Again, the machinable grades are not used in cold heading, and in drawing they require small drafts. Die costs may be high because of the tendency of the austenitic grades (particularly 304) to stick and to cause galling. This can be offset by a judicious choice of lubricant.

Among stainless steel wires (produced by cold drawing and intermediate annealing) the austenitic grades are the most common, and among these, 302 and 304 predominate.

Hot Forming

Many stainless steel fabricators use cold forming processes for bending and shaping sheet, but hot forming falls into the rather specialized operation of the stainless mill and forge. The subject of hot working, then, touches a rather small number of stainless steel fabricators, and those whom it does interest are specialists in the field. Therefore the subject will be dealt with here in very general terms.

The standard grades of stainless, in all classes, can be hot worked, although the process becomes more difficult as the alloy content increases. Figure 6.2 gives recommended forging temperatures. Because ferritic and austenitic stainless steels do not undergo a phase transformation during cooling, the maximum working temperature and the finishing temperature have to be more carefully controlled than in the hot working of plain carbon steels. The thermal conductivity of stainless steels is lower than that of plain carbon steels, particularly at temperatures below 1000 F; hence the time taken to reach temperature is longer, and soaking times are therefore greater. The martensitic steels, because they may initially be in a hardened condition, require particularly slow heating rates prior to working, to avoid cracking.

Martensitic Stainless Steels. Heating is usually accomplished in two stages. The first—up to about 1500 F—is slow, so that a uniform tem-

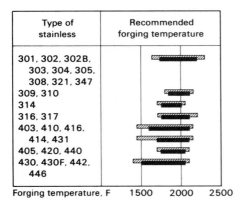

Type of stainless	Recommended forging temperature
301, 302, 302B, 303, 304, 305, 308, 321, 347	
309, 310	
314	
316, 317	
403, 410, 416, 414, 431	
405, 420, 440	
430, 430F, 442, 446	

Forging temperature, F   1500   2000   2500

Fig. 6.2. Recommended temperature ranges for forging stainless steels. The cross-hatched limits show temperature ranges that have been recommended by some but on which there is not general agreement. Solid bars are generally accepted

perature is attained across the piece: transformation and thermal-expansion stresses are minimized. Subsequently, the piece is heated to forming temperature (see Fig. 6.2), and after forming, it is removed from the forge or rolls and held at 1550 F, and then slowly cooled so that air hardening is prevented.

The lower-carbon martensitic steels (403, 410, 416) have a wide range of forging temperatures (as Fig. 6.2 indicates). 420 and 440 require more control; 431 requires special care during cooling because it is particularly susceptible to cracking. In all grades finishing must occur above the transformation temperature (about 1500 F).

Ferritic Stainless Steels. Heating to temperature is similar, but subsequent cooling is not critical in the nonhardening grades. However, a stress relief at about 500 to 600 F will remove forging stresses. Although grain growth occurs rapidly in the upper part of the soaking range, working can be continued to a low finishing temperature (about 1400 F) and hence grain refinement occurs. An exception is 405, which develops grain-boundary weakness at temperature. This grade is therefore finished at a higher temperature. Compared with the hardenable grades, the steels scale less, because they have a higher chromium content.

Austenitic Stainless Steels. Two factors lead to different hot working procedures for the austenitic grades: (*a*) the higher alloy content leads to greater hot strength, and hence, in order that hot working be possible with economical energy consumption, higher working temperatures are employed (see Fig. 6.2), and (*b*) because of the effect of sensitization (Chapter 4), all grades with the exception of the stabilized compositions must be finished above the sensitizing range of temperature (whose upper limit is about 1600 F) and cooled as rapidly as possible to 1000 F.

Heating procedures are similar to those already described, and time at temperature in oxidizing atmospheres should be held to a minimum so that scaling is not excessive. After hot working, the piece should be fully annealed. (As pointed out previously in Table 4.4, austenitic stainless steels are generally annealed between 1850 and 2050 F.)

Cutting

Cold Shearing Processes. This section is restricted to shearing and blanking. Cutting as a machining operation (turning, milling, etc.) is considered in a later section. Shearing and blanking are similar operations in that the metal is cut by the shearing action of a moving edge. In shearing, a single moving blade or two opposed blades move against the metal. In blanking, the action of a punch and die cuts out a shape in sheet, generally for subsequent forming.

Stainless steel sheet, because it is stronger than plain carbon steel sheet, requires greater power in shearing: power requirements can be based upon the assumption that the shearing force is about three quarters of the ultimate tensile strength of the steel.

Because of their work-hardening tendency, the austenitic grades require a punch or shear action that takes the moving edge through the sheet thickness: the cut part does not drop off after shearing part way, as it does in plain carbon sheet. In order that the effects of work hardening do not lead to a poor edge, blades must be accurately set, well sharpened, and clean. Clearances for austenitic stainless steels are usually less than those for plain carbon steels, and run about 5% of sheet thickness. The relief angle must be kept small so that cutting edges do not chip, and hold-downs must be particularly secure.

The more brittle ferritic grades may be warmed prior to cutting.

Hot Processes. Stainless steels can be cut—inaccurately and with difficulty—by melting processes in which a standard gas torch or metallic arc is directed on to the metal. The constitution of the steel in the heat-affected zone is changed according to the principles set down in Chapter 4 and discussed later in connection with welding processes.

The formation of chromium oxide impedes cutting and necessitates a lengthy contact time; hence heat effects may be pronounced. To reduce the total heat input and to produce cleaner edges, methods commonly used today inject flux or iron powder into the cutting flame or arc. In oxyacetylene cutting, powder is introduced into the oxygen stream. In oxyarc cutting, oxygen is blown through a hollow electrode, which is flux-coated.

Joining

Of the methods of joining stainless steels, fusion arc welding is the most frequently encountered, and it will therefore be treated most fully. Although their increasing significance should not be underplayed, electron-beam and laser welding are not described; at this stage of the game the interested reader should refer to current periodicals.

Mechanical Fasteners. Stainless steel fasteners are available in a full range of materials, as bolts, nuts, studs, and rivets. Their successful incorporation into a joint involves considerations of mechanical design (which fall outside the scope of this book) and of corrosion tolerance (which is covered in Chapter 8).

Brazing. Brazing alloys are usually composed of copper, silver, and zinc, and their action is to flow on to and partially into the metals that are being joined, forming a permanent bond between the pieces. The temperature of brazing is (by a quite arbitrary definition) above 800 F but below the melting temperature of the metals being joined.

All the stainless steels can be brazed. Joints must be clean, but no fluxes are required. The disadvantages of brazing arise mainly through two inevitable occurrences:

1. The brazing metal must, if the joint is to be effective, diffuse into the stainless steel. Hence we must be prepared for a loss of corrosion resistance in the area of the joint, which may be exaggerated through the galvanic effect of the two dissimilar materials. High-temperature brazing alloys may penetrate grain boundaries and cause severe weakening, and brazing stressed parts may lead to subsequent stress-corrosion cracking (see Chapter 8).

2. The flow temperature of copper-base brazing alloys is above 2000 F. At such temperatures the austenitic grades (unless they are stabilized) are subject to sensitization, and the martensitic grades will, if they are not slowly cooled, harden in a region immediately adjacent to the joint. The regions further from the joint will have effectively become tempered, with a consequent loss of strength.

Soldering. The mechanism of soldering is similar to that of brazing, but the temperature of the process is lower. The soft solders flow at temperatures about 400 F; the silver solders flow at higher temperatures and may, indeed, fall into the category of brazing alloys.

Stainless steels can be soft soldered and silver soldered. At these lower temperatures, fluxes are required to remove the chromic oxide film from the stainless so that the solder can flow and penetrate the metal. The fluxes are usually very active, and residues must be thoroughly removed after the joint is completed. No problems of sensitization, hardening, or tempering arise at the lower temperatures involved in soldering. However, soldered joints are not so strong as brazed joints, and the strength of the joint decreases (in general terms) as the melting temperature of the solder is lowered. The corrosion resistance of the assembly is reduced— for the reasons already given.

Resistance Welding. In resistance welding, which is a forge-welding process, metal is heated by the passage of electric current (directly applied or induced) to a temperature below its melting point and the joint is made by the application of pressure. No filler metal is added. There are many variations in the way in which resistance heating of the metal is accomplished, in the means by which pressure is applied, and in the type of joint being made. In seam welding the workpieces are continuously fed beneath a rotating electrode, which supplies the power, or beneath an electrical induction coil, which induces a current in the steel. In spot welding two electrodes supply both the heating current and the pressure. Resistance welding is generally used on production items: it is not economically employed where a variety of short-run items are involved.

The good forgeability of most of the stainless grades, coupled with their high electrical resistance and low thermal conductivity, favors resistance welding methods. Because no filler metal is added, no galvanic problems arise in subsequent corrosive service. We will not enumerate the difficulties associated with the various grades when heated: matters of sensitization, hardening, and tempering should now be familiar.

Fusion Welding. In fusion welding, parent metal is actually melted and filler metal is usually (though not always) added. In fusion arc welding, heat is supplied by the arc struck between an electrode and the job. This method of welding is most commonly used in fabricating shops and in the field where the variety of work is wide.

The structure that results from a fusion weld contains a small casting (the weld bead) and a heat-affected zone adjacent to it. Thus the properties of the weldment are determined by these two regions. Contrary to a common prejudice, the properties of castings are not necessarily worse than the properties of a forging: in fact, *for a given grain size and constitution*, the properties of the casting and of the forging are equivalent. Of couse, if the weld is a poor one and the bead contains dirt or is cracked, then its properties will be correspondingly unsatisfactory. The same may be said of a forging.

There is a distinct difference between weld beads of the ferritic and austenitic stainless steels (and these are the most frequently welded) and weld beads of the carbon and low-alloy steels. In plain carbon and low-alloy steels, as in the martensitic class of stainless steels, the material undergoes a transformation on heating and cooling. A single weld bead laid down will consist of unrefined grains, usually of a columnar shape (Fig. 6.3). If this bead is heated above the transformation temperature (about 1600 F in plain carbon steels, about 1500 F in martensitic stainless steels) and is subsequently cooled, grain refinement occurs. This process happens to each pass as a subsequent pass is applied (Fig. 6.3),

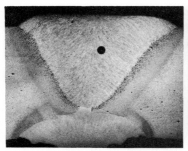 

Fig. 6.3. Structure of weld bead in mild steel. (Left) As-cast structure. (Round black mark is a hardness indentation.) (Right) Refinement in structure with successive passes in multipass welding. 2.5×. From A. Hanson and J. Gordon Parr, "The Engineer's Guide to Steel," Addison-Wesley, 1965

and in this way, the original properties of the weld bead, which are influenced by the large, unidirectional grain size, are improved. The initial columnar grain structure is less tough and ductile, particularly in a direction perpendicular to the length of the grain. After heat treatment (conveniently effected by subsequent weld passes) the grain size is smaller and randomly oriented. In fact, the grain size and shape are similar to those of a normalized product, and hence the properties are similar. Any inferiority of properties in a single-pass weld bead compared with a forging of the same material (if it is assumed that there are no macroscopic defects in either) is due to the large grain size of the weld bead.

No grain refinement is possible in the austenitic and ferritic classes, because they undergo no thermal transformation. Therefore, the structure of the weld bead as laid down persists. It is important, therefore, to avoid excessive grain growth, because this cannot be subsequently corrected. If the importance of a good weld-bead casting is borne in mind together with the effects of heat upon the parent-metal structure, a reasonable analysis of fusion welding stainless steel can be made.

Four main processes of fusion arc welding stainless steel will be described:

Metal-Arc Welding. An arc is struck between a current-carrying electrode and the workpiece. The electrode supplies filler metal to the joint, and is coated with flux, which melts off to protect and cleanse the weld. The heat of the arc melts the steel in the vicinity of the joint and makes it an integral part of the weld-bead casting—this is a necessary criterion of all fusion processes. Although both direct and alternating current can be used, direct current with reverse polarity (electrode, positive; work, negative) is most common for gages up to $^3/_{16}$ in. Straight polarity is often used for heavier gages.

Submerged-Arc Welding. A wire electrode carries the current and supplies filler metal, as before, but it is bare. The flux protection of the weld is supplied by granulated material that is separately fed into the joint region, and the arc is struck beneath the surface of the flux. This method allows the use of higher welding currents, and hence welding speed is increased. It is more suited to continuous operation, where economics permit the larger installation and setup costs.

Tungsten Inert-Gas Arc Welding (TIG). An arc is produced by a tungsten electrode, which is not consumed, and filler metal in the form of bare wire is introduced to the joint via a torch, through which flows a protective gas. The inert gas is usually argon or helium; carbon dioxide, more commonly used for other ferrous materials, is sometimes used, although the corrosion resistance of the welds is said to be inferior.

Metal Inert-Gas Arc Welding (MIG). This process is similar to the TIG process in that inert gas is used as protection. However, filler wire, continuously fed, replaces the tungsten electrode. Like the submerged-arc process, it is suited to production runs.

Weldability. The thermal conductivity of stainless steels is about half that of plain carbon and low-alloy grades. (The fraction is lower at lower temperatures and greater at elevated temperatures.) Hence heat is not dissipated so rapidly from the weld region, and welding current for a given thickness and speed, is less. *Skip* or *step-back* welding techniques (Fig. 6.4) minimize the local concentration of heat and hence reduce susceptibility to cracking and warpage during cooling. Heat dissipation can be increased by use of copper chill bars held against the parent metal adjacent to the weld bead.

To ensure sound welds, particularly in the austenitic grades, welding fixtures must be firm, or, alternatively, tack welds should be made at frequent intervals.

As in all welding procedures, the joint design must allow satisfactory deposition of the filler metal and fusion with the parent edges. In welding stainless steel the joint design should also encourage heat dissipation. For this reason, the use of bevels is common in smaller gages, which, in plain carbon steel, might be welded as a square-edge butt. The bevel

Fig. 6.4. Sequences in skip and step-back welding. Arrows indicate length and direction of weld passes; numbers indicate sequence of weld passes

permits the use of several light passes and so avoids the high temperatures that would be reached in a single, heavy pass.

Cleaning and edge preparation, important in any welding process, are particularly critical in stainless steel work. It is important that contamination from grease and oil be avoided (so that corrosion resistance will not be reduced through subsequent carburization). The use of carbon steel files and brushes is not recommended, because these may leave fragments of high-carbon material adhering to the stainless steel, and, in filing, some carbon pickup by solid-state diffusion is to be expected, because the surface temperatures reached during filing are very high. Therefore stainless steel tools are customarily used during final preparation and cleaning of edges.

After welding, the job should be thoroughly cleaned of fluxes and spatter. And since the article is probably to be used in corrosive service, grinding and buffing are frequently called for so that surface irregularities will not encourage localized attack. Finishing stainless steel surfaces is discussed in a later part of this chapter.

Martensitic Stainless Steels. The tendency to form martensite during cooling, and hence the propensity to cracking, can be offset by preheating, which reduces the subsequent cooling rate from welding temperature. However, because of the high hardenability of the material, it is probable that some martensite will be formed, and postheating is generally practiced.

One method of postheating involves heating to about 1400 F and cooling to about 1100 F at a rate that does not exceed 50 F per hour. Subsequent cooling can be rapid. Alternatively, a higher-temperature postheating, involving heating to at least 1550 F, with slow cooling to 1100 F can be adopted. In the first type of post-heat-treatment martensite is decomposed to ferrite; in the second type, the steel is taken into the austenite region and, by the slow cooling process, allowed to transform to ferrite instead of to martensite. In both heat treatments residual stresses arising from the welding process are relieved, though more completely in the high-temperature treatment.

Naturally, these heat treatment processes will affect the mechanical properties of the steel adjacent to the weld, and a complete heat treatment of the entire weldment may be necessary to restore properties—although, of course, this is not always practicable.

The filler metal for welds (that is, the welding rod or wire) can be of identical composition to the steel to be welded, but welds in the martensitic stainless steels are quite commonly made using an austenitic filler. The weld bead therefore has higher ductility and lower strength than the parent metal that surrounds it.

Ferritic Stainless Steels.   The three major difficulties associated with the welding of steels in this grade are (*a*) excessive grain growth at high temperature, (*b*) sensitization, when the steel is cooled from temperatures above 1700 F, and (*c*) lack of ductility.

Grain coarsening is a principal contributor to the lack of ductility. But the problem may be contributed to by the sigma phase and by 885 F embrittlement (p 47) and, in the high-carbon low-chromium grades, by the formation of martensite in the heat-affected zone during cooling. No heat treatment restores a fine grain. The sigma phase can be removed by heating to about 2000 F and cooling sufficiently rapidly to avoid the occurrence of 885 F embrittlement (p 47). Heating to about 1500 F followed by rapid cooling improves ductility, probably because it removes 885 F embrittlement and restores a sensitized structure to one that will not be susceptible to intergranular attack. It may be argued that heating to 1500 F will encourage sigma-phase formation. While this is true, the phase forms fairly slowly—it is usually more bothersome in the highly alloyed grades of the 300 series, and is discussed again in the next section.

The "truly" ferritic grade 446 is particularly susceptible to grain growth and loss of ductility, as is 442 and the nonstandard grade 443. 430, which (despite its place in the ferritic class) is slightly hardenable, is less affected. 405 is most easily welded, but its lower chromium content reduces corrosion resistance, and the grade is in much less demand than the popular 430 ferritic stainless.

Filler metal in ferritic joints can be of either a similar composition or an austenitic material. The austenitic filler (308, 309, 310) produces welds of greater ductility and toughness and is particularly helpful in welding 446, but the effect of the dissimilar material may reduce corrosion resistance and lead to other problems through differing coefficients of thermal expansion. When austenitic filler is used, postheating may be eliminated.

Austenitic Stainless Steels.   The 200- and 300-series austenitic compositions are the most weldable. The problems that arise relate mainly to the possibilities of sensitization in the heat-affected zone, and this can be counteracted by the methods described in Chapter 4.

No preheating is necessary; postheating, if it is performed at all, is usually for the purpose of redissolving precipitated carbides and so restoring corrosion resistance. However, post-heat-treatment is also used for the stress relief of components that are to be used in environments that may cause stress-corrosion cracking and for the stress relief of parts that are fabricated from clad material. (The use of clad stainless in pressure vessels and other equipment may involve conforming to a code that demands the stress relief of any carbon-welded structure.) Because sensitization occurs at temperatures between 800 and 1500 F, with a maximum rate at about

1200 F, stress-relief heat treatments avoid this range whenever possible if the stainless steel is subject to sensitization. If the steel is heated above the sensitizing range, subsequent cooling through it should be rapid. (Stress-relief heat treatments for the austenitic stainless steels have been given previously in Chapter 4.)

Susceptibility to sensitization is minimal in the extra-low-carbon grades (designated L) and in the stabilized grades 347 and 321; it increases in other grades as the ratio of carbon to chromium increases—and, because of the permitted range of compositions, precise predictions cannot be made. However, those steels with a maximum carbon content of 0.08% (304, 308, 316) are generally less susceptible than those with a maximum of 0.15% (for example, 301 and 302) or 0.25% (310).

'Knife-line' attack may arise in the parent metal of stabilized weldments. Here, although the metal contains columbium or titanium, sensitization occurs because of the solution of these elements and their inability to form carbides during subsequent rapid cooling. Then, as lower temperatures are reached, chromium carbides form, leading to sensitization. The effect is found in the heat-affected zone very close to the weld bead.

The coefficient of expansion of austenitic stainless steel is higher than that of plain carbon steels; hence the amount of thermal contraction is greater. Precautions to avoid bead cracking and to minimize distortion— sound fixtures, tack welding, skip or step-back welding, copper chills, minimum heat input, small weld passes—are thus demanded.

The austenitic grades may contain some ferrite: we remember that the austenitic structure, while it is persistent, is not in the strict sense of the word stable. For example, it may break down as a result of cold work, as we have already mentioned. Ferrite is commonly produced in an austenitic weld bead; the amount present depends to some extent upon the cooling rate and subsequent heat treatment, but more upon the composition.

It is generally held that 4% ferrite in welds is an effective means of offsetting a grain-boundary weakness that develops in austenite at high temperatures and leads to fissuring. The amount of ferrite present can be assessed by magnetic methods or (if a sample is available) by metallographic examination; the amount of ferrite to be expected can be determined from the Schaeffler diagram (Fig. 6.5). Figure 6.6 shows what are described as desirable and excessive amounts of the phase. Welding-electrode compositions are chosen in relation to the amount of ferrite that is desired. Too great an amount of ferrite can lead to several undesirable effects, among which are a lowering of high-temperature strength and of corrosion resistance. Another danger of high ferrite content is the encouragement of the formation of the sigma phase.

Sigma, formed between 1000 and 1600 F, reduces corrosion resistance

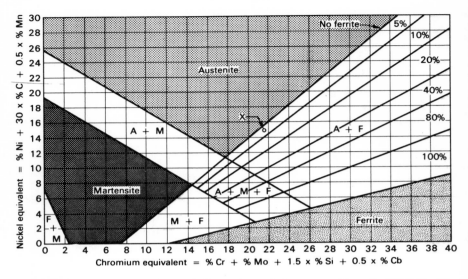

Example: Point X on the diagram indicates the equivalent composition of a 318 (316 with columbium) weld deposit containing 0.07% carbon, 1.55% manganese, 0.57% silicon, 18.02% chromium, 11.87% nickel, 2.16% molybdenum, and 0.80% columbium. Each of these percentages was multiplied by the "potency factor" indicated for the element in question along the axes of the diagram, in order to determine the chromium equivalent and the nickel equivalent. When these were plotted, as point X, the constitution of the weld was indicated as austenite plus from 0 to 5% ferrite. Magnetic analysis of the actual sample revealed an average ferrite content of 2%. For austenite-plus-ferrite structures, the diagram predicts the percentage ferrite within 4% for the following corrosion-resistant steels: CH-20, CH-20C, CK-20, CF-12M, and CF-8MC.

Fig. 6.5. Schaeffler diagram for estimating ferrite content from composition

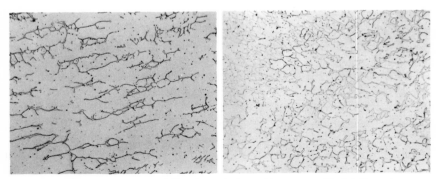

Fig. 6.6. Ferrite in a 308 weld bead. (Left) Desirable amount. (Right) Excessive amount

and ductility. While its formation in iron-chromium-nickel alloys is slow, the presence of molybdenum, silicon and, most important, columbium, speeds the reaction, and its formation is more rapid from ferrite than from austenite. It can be removed by heating at 1900 to 2000 F and cooling— a process that, at the same time, redissolves carbides and removes any sensitization. The appearance of the sigma phase in weld deposits is shown in Fig. 6.7.

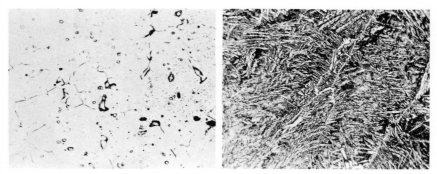

Fig. 6.7. Sigma phase in a weld bead of (left) a stainless steel containing 25% chromium and 20% nickel and (right) a stainless steel containing 26% chromium, 16% nickel, and 5% molybdenum. 375 ×

Precipitation-Hardening Stainless Steels. Martensitic precipitation-hardening stainless steels generally require no preheating or postheating. In thick sections, however, post-heat-treatment may be necessary to regain properties lost by overaging, and, depending upon design, the fully hardened steel may distort or crack during welding—in which case preliminary softening by overaging is required. Weld filler-metal compositions are similar to parent metal.

During fusion welding, there is a tendency for the aluminum contained in the steel to oxidize. This can be minimized by using tungsten inert-gas arc welding methods, with as low heat input as practicable.

Semi-austenitic precipitation-hardening stainless steels also are suited to inert-gas welding methods, and no preheating or postheating may be required. However, weld ductility may be low, and aging at 1100 F is necessary to improve it. If optimum properties are sought, the weldment should be refrigerated and subsequently aged.

Austenitic precipitation-hardening stainless steels should be in the annealed condition, and are weldable by inert-gas methods. Titanium, as well as aluminum, is prone to oxidize during welding.

Table 6.4. Compositions of Welding Electrodes for Welding Stainless Cladding of Stainless-Clad Steels

Clad-ding	Electrodes	
	First Pass(a)	Subsequent passes
301	25 Cr–20 Ni or 25 Cr–12 Ni	25 Cr–20 Ni or 25 Cr–12 Ni(b)
302	25 Cr–20 Ni or 25 Cr–12 Ni	25 Cr–20 Ni or 25 Cr–12 Ni(b)
304	25 Cr–20 Ni or 25 Cr–12 Ni	25 Cr–20 Ni or 25 Cr–12 Ni(b)
304L	25 Cr–20 Ni–Cb or 25 Cr–12 Ni–Cb	25 Cr–20 Ni–Cb or 25 Cr–12 Ni–Cb(c)
308	25 Cr–20 Ni or 25 Cr–12 Ni	25 Cr–20 Ni or 25 Cr–12 Ni(b)
309	25 Cr–20 Ni	25 Cr–20 Ni
310	25 Cr–20 Ni	25 Cr–20 Ni
316	25 Cr–20 Ni–Mo	25 Cr–20 Ni–Mo or 25 Cr–12 Ni–Mo(d)
321	25 Cr–20 Ni–Cb or 25 Cr–12 Ni–Cb	25 Cr–20 Ni–Cb or 25 Cr–12 Ni–Cb(c)
347	25 Cr–20 Ni–Cb or 25 Cr–12 Ni–Cb	25 Cr–20 Ni–Cb or 25 Cr–12 Ni–Cb(c)
405	25 Cr–20 Ni or 25 Cr–12 Ni	25 Cr–20 Ni or 25 Cr–12 Ni
410	25 Cr–20 Ni or 25 Cr–12 Ni	25 Cr–20 Ni or 25 Cr–12 Ni
430	25 Cr–20 Ni or 25 Cr–12 Ni	25 Cr–20 Ni or 25 Cr–12 Ni

(a) Over exposed plain carbon or low-alloy steel weld bead
(b) Cover pass may be 19 Cr–9 Ni.
(c) Cover pass may be 19 Cr–9 Ni–Cb.
(d) Cover pass may be 19 Cr–9 Ni–Mo.

Machinable Stainless Steels. Problems of porosity and segregation arise when the free-machining grades are welded. However, special electrodes (312) are available that, with the careful exclusion of hydrogen from the weld, assist welding.

Stainless-Clad Material. In welding clad material it is important to avoid the transfer of carbon from the backup to the stainless. Usually the plain carbon side is welded first, with carbon steel filler. The weld is then ground out from the stainless steel side, and stainless filler—usually of higher alloy content than the parent metal, to overcome dilution effects—is applied. A guide to welding clad materials is given in Table 6.4.

Machining

The machinability of standard stainless steels can be summarized in the following way, although wide variations of performance are to be expected when different machining processes and conditions are employed:

1. The martensitic stainless steels are usually machined (except for fine work after heat treatment) in the annealed condition. Their machinability is generally intermediate to the ferritic and austenitic grades.

2. The ferritic grades are easiest to machine.

3. The austenitic grades are gummy and give the most difficulty.

4. Improved machinability (in all classes) is obtained through additions of lead, sulfur, selenium, or phosphorus. While some of these grades

fall into the AISI classification, many others are nonstandard, and are available from manufacturers' lists.

As with any material that tends to stick and gall during machining, the work and tool must be firmly held and lubrication must be effective. Because of work-hardening tendencies in ferritic and most particularly in austenitic grades, a positive cut must be made at all times. If the tool is allowed to run idle against the surface of the job, hard spots that will subsequently be difficult to machine will develop and will cause a rough finish and excessive tool wear. This should be borne in mind during reaming operations: it is important to leave enough material to be cut during reaming.

Machining equipment should be overpowered compared with carbon steel requirements. Chatter and whipping must be avoided, and for this reason drill bits and reamers should be kept as short as possible. Turning tools should have ample clearances; negative rake offers maximum sup-

Table 6.5. Geometry of Tools Used in Machining Stainless Steels

Tool	Geometry
Drills	Included angle 130 to 140° Cutting-edge clearance 6 to 15° Webs thin
Reamers	Spiral fluted preferable Lead in chamfer 30° minimum with 2 to 3° on land below chamfer Clearance angle about 7° Land widths narrow
Taps	Chamfer 9° minimum Positive rake (hook) 15° Spiral flutes
Threading dies	Positive rake (hook) about 15° for straight threads, up to 30° for circular and tangent chasers
Milling cutters	Positive rake 5 to 20° (a negative rake on carbide cutters) Clearance angle 5 to 10°
Saws	About 8 teeth per inch for heavy stock, more for lighter sections Reciprocating saws must clear work on return stroke

port; a groove for chip curling helps to eliminate long clogging chips. A large lathe tool, with a radius cut on the nose, helps to increase life by aiding heat dissipation. Table 6.5 and Figs. 6.8 and 6.9 give a few guides on tool geometry.

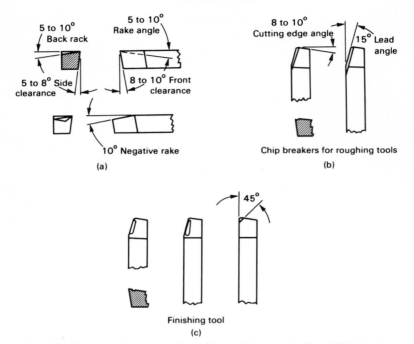

Fig. 6.8. *Geometry of turning tools used for stainless steels. From "Fabricating Stainless Steel," R. E. Paret, The Tool Engineer, Jan. 1959*

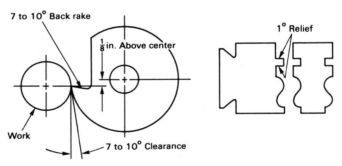

Fig. 6.9. *Geometry of form tools used for stainless steels. Side clearance reduces chatter and helps balance end thrust. From "Fabricating Stainless Steel," R. E. Paret, The Tool Engineer, Jan. 1959*

Because of the low thermal conductivity of stainless steels, ample cutting fluid must be used (except in friction sawing). Sulfur-base oils are generally used for heavy cuts at low speeds. For high speeds and with lighter cuts, water-soluble oil is preferable, particularly with carbide tools.

Finishing

Standard mill finishes for stainless steel sheet are listed in Table 6.6. The job of the fabricator is often to grind and polish welded areas so that they blend with the original sheet—which, of course, is protected as far as

Table 6.6. Mill Finishes for Stainless Steel Sheet

Finish No.	Description	Use	
		As final finish	As starting finish
1	Frosty white. Produced by hot rolling followed by annealing and descaling	High-temperature or industrial use	When appearance not important or surface affected by high temperature
2D	Dull cold rolled finish, similar to No. 1 but brighter. Produced by cold rolling, annealing, and descaling. The dull finish may result from descaling or may be developed by a final, light, cold roll pass on dull rolls.	Industrial applications	When severe drawing is followed by polishing
2B	Bright, dense. Produced the same as No. 2D, except that the annealed and descaled sheet receives a final, light, cold roll pass on polished rolls	Architectural applications; industrial equipment	When light forming is followed by polishing
3	Bright. A polished finish obtained with abrasives (100-mesh). Sheets may or may not be polished during fabrication	Not normally used	See "Description"
4	Bright, good luster. Sheets are finished with 120- to 150-mesh abrasive	Architectural trim, restaurant, and sanitary equipment	Base for No. 6, 7, and 8 finishes (see below)
6	Dull satin finish, lower reflectivity than No. 4. Produced by Tampico brushing the No. 4 finish	Decorative use without high reflectivity	When forming operations will not mar surface or can be blended easily
7	High reflectivity. Produced by buffing finely ground surface. "Grit" lines not removed	Decorative use	When forming operations will not mar surface or can be blended easily
8	Mirror finish. Obtained by polishing and buffing extensively. Surface is free of grit lines	Decorative use	When forming operations will not mar surface or can be blended easily

possible during fabrication. Finish No. 4, a general-purpose polished finish, is the most popular finish. It is popular in architecture because higher polishes give too intense reflections and are diffiult to maintain during fabrication.

To reduce the amount of finishing, care should be taken during fabrication to avoid unnecessary damage. Adhesive paper can be applied, and mills will supply stainless sheet with a protective plastic coating that can be peeled off later.

If a part is to be heat treated, organic materials—including finger prints —must be removed, or a pattern will be burned into the surface. They can be cleaned off with organic solvents, or a grease of sodium carbonate applied on a soft cloth.

Decorative Finishes. Oil canning, an optical distortion, arises through thermal expansion and contraction of flat stainless sheet panels. If fully reflecting panels are essential, then they must be sufficiently well supported to avoid buckling: by using heavier gage, by backing light-gage sheet with heavy plate or board, by reducing the continuous areas of flat surfaces. Alternatively, and if reflection is not required, a shallow die-pressed texture can be embossed on to the steel by rolling.

Although coatings are not necessary for corrosion protection in atmospheric environments, colored coatings offer attractive architectural possibilities. The coating is durable, because the underlying metal resists corrosion, and highlighted patterns can be obtained by applying the coating to a rolled pattern and then removing the coating from raised portions by grinding or polishing. The coating can be an enamel, an organic coating, or a blackening obtained by one of a number of chemical processes.

Both mechanical abrasives and chemical etchants can be used to produce a roughened design on a polished plate. The chemical process can be carried out by offset printing: the print, which is inked on to the sheet from the master plate, acts as an adherent for an acid-resisting substance (usually resin, pitch, and asphaltum), so that when the etchant is subsequently applied it only attacks the non-inked areas. Acid etches commonly used contain (*a*) 75 parts hydrochloric acid, 25 parts water, and 5 parts nitric acid by volume with 20% ferric chloride by weight, or (*b*) about 10 to 20% nitric acid and 3 to 5% hydrofluoric acid in water. Hardened parts should not be etched chemically or they may crack, and sensitized austenitic parts will suffer intergranular corrosion.

Descaling. After heat treatment the removal of scale may be necessary, and there is no single, simple method that can be recommended.

Pickling. Acid mixtures depend upon the activity of hydrofluoric acid (or with more caution, hydrochloric acid) mixed with nitric acid (which, of course, is a passivator), in water. Concentrations of about 15% nitric, with 1 to 3% hydrofluoric, in water are used at about 120 to 140 F. Preliminary pickling in 10% sulfuric acid at 150 F softens the scale.

Other pickling agents are available. All should be tested to determine best operating conditions prior to use, and users should familiarize themselves with the dangers of handling acids and the precautions to be taken, before embarking upon a pickling process.

Caustic Descaling. Proprietary processes that depend upon the action of fused salts on the scale are used for caustic descaling. In the du Pont sodium hydride process the scale is reduced; in the Virgo process molten sodium nitrate disintegrates the scale. Both processes involve water quenching to remove adhering scale by thermal shock, and an acid treatment to neutralize any remaining caustic.

Sand and Grit Blasting. This method is suitable for heavy pieces and is usually followed by a pickling process. Plain carbon steel shot should not be used.

Polishing. Fine grinding and buffing, electrolytic methods, or barrel finishing can be used for polishing. In buffing, a series of increasingly fine abrasives is applied by wheels or belts. Barrel finishing involves tumbling the articles in a suspension of polishing abrasive—and is limited to small parts. Electropolishing, which is particularly suited to the production line, depends upon the stainless steel part being the anode in an electrochemical cell. Minor surface asperities, which constitute "roughness," are removed during a controlled dissolution process, but major irregularities are not removed. An over-all thousandth of an inch of metal is generally

Table 6.7. Details of Electropolishing Baths Used in Electropolishing Stainless Steels

Process	Composition of bath	Temp of bath, F	Current density, amp/sq dm
Battelle process–I	Sulfuric acid, 15% Phosphoric acid, 63%	81–176	>5
Battelle process–II	Phosphoric acid, 56% Chromic anhydride, 12%	81–176	10–100
Electropol process (Charlesworth)(a)	Sulfuric acid, 55% Phosphoric acid, 22% Aniline, 2–3%	....	>5
Weisberg and Levin	Lactic acid, 33% Phosphoric acid, 40% Sulfuric acid, 13.5%	158–199	7.5–30
W. J. Neill	Sulfuric acid, 48% Hydrofluoric acid, 14% Oxalic acid, 1%	140–169	5–25

(a) Gives good results only on austenitic steels

removed during electropolishing, and a mirror finish can be obtained. Details of electropolishing baths are given in Table 6.7.

Powder Metallurgy

The fabrication of shapes from metal powders originated in the refractory metals that could be shaped in no other way, and probably the earliest commercially produced powder-metallurgy part was tungsten wire for lamp filaments.

The principle of powder fabrication is to compact the powder (whose particle size is usually between 1 and 200 microns) and then to sinter it. Further shaping operations may follow sintering. Today, the technique involves many more metals than the difficult refractory ones. For example, there are more than 100 different powder-metallurgy parts (mostly iron-base) in use in modern American cars.

The advantages of powder-metallurgy processes include not only the ability to deal with high melting-point materials, but the production of precise shapes with reduced machining costs, the possibility of developing new composite materials or dispersion-strengthened metals, and the ease of controlling porosity for specific applications, such as bearings and filters. An attractive possibility to the potential producer of metal parts is that he avoids the equipment associated with molten metal.

Obviously the application of powder techniques depends upon their economy compared with other fabrication methods, but this is not the place for an analysis. We will simply point out that stainless steel powders are available in most grades. At present most are made by atomizing a liquid-metal stream. The techniques for compacting and sintering are becoming established, and literature is available from stainless steel powder manufacturers.

At present, a principal disadvantage of stainless steel powder-made parts is their inferior corrosion resistance. New variables are introduced through the effect of the atmosphere in the sintering operations, and (probably) contamination by the lubricant used during compacting. However, the general technology of powder metallurgy is advancing rapidly, and the stainless steel fabricator and user should not overlook the possibilities offered by powder processes.

Chapter 7

Principles of Corrosion

While man sweats to reduce the earth's minerals to metals, Mother Nature does her best to convert metals back to minerals again. Iron oxide is mined, concentrated, fed to the blast furnace and into the steelmaking unit, rolled into shape, and used in the construction of a building. Air and rain then work on the steel, convert it to iron oxide, and wash it back into the earth.

Metallic corrosion can be considered as the undesirable reaction of a metal or alloy with its environment. The environment can be gaseous or liquid, but it is convenient to consider the general case of corrosion to involve the reactions of a metal with an aqueous solution. This permits the most straightforward treatment of corrosion problems according to the fundamental laws of physics and chemistry. In this way the more complicated cases of corrosion of metals and alloys in gaseous environments, in organic liquids, and in liquid metals can be dealt with according to predetermined principles.

Mechanism of Corrosion

Corrosion mechanisms involve an oxidation and a reduction reaction. That is, there is an increase in valence of the corroding material—the oxidation reaction—and there is a decrease in valence of a constituent of the corrosive environment—the reduction reaction. (The term "oxidation reaction" is not to be confused with the terms "oxidizing acid" or "oxidizing condition," which involve an actual contribution of oxygen in a chemical reaction involving the formation of an oxide.) Each of these reactions can be divided into two individual processes for which equilibrium conditions can be defined. Thus corrosion reactions can be subjected to the laws of chemistry. And since the oxidation reaction involves the release of electrons on the corroding metal surface and the reduction reaction involves the consumption of electrons, there must be a movement of electrons in a corrosion process. Therefore corrosion reactions can be subjected to the laws of electricity. All corrosion processes can be considered as electrochemical in nature. Although we are concerned with the stifling of corrosion reactions rather than with their stimulation, it is necessary to determine the driving force that sustains these spontaneous processes.

Corrosion in an Aqueous Environment

When a metal is in contact with an aqueous solution containing its dissolved ions, there is a movement of atoms from the metal surface into solution, as dissolved ions, with the liberation of electrons at the metal surface. There is also a movement in the opposite direction of ions from solution to the metal surface, where they reunite with electrons to become atoms again. Eventually, the processes in both directions reach a state of equilibrium, and the metal acquires an electric charge.

Standard Electrode Potential. The magnitude of the electrical charge varies with each metal, and for a given metal it varies with surface condition and prior heat treatment and mechanical working. The charge can be measured, and if a standard set of conditions is maintained, the magnitude of this electrical charge can be related to the driving force of a corrosion reaction involving a similar dissolution of the metal.

Consider a strip of zinc at 25 C (77.0 F) and 1 atm pressure dipping into an aqueous solution of zinc chloride containing zinc ions at unit activity. (Activity, the effective concentration, is the product of molar concentration and an activity coefficient.) This is a set of standard conditions for a zinc electrode. Now, consider a strip of copper at 25 C (77.0 F) and 1 atm pressure dipping into an aqueous solution of copper sulphate containing cupric ions at unit activity. This is a standard copper electrode. Let the two individual solutions be joined internally by a salt bridge and let the two electrodes be joined externally, as shown in Fig. 7.1. A current will flow in the wire, zinc will dissolve (oxidation) at the zinc electrode and copper will plate out (reduction) at the copper electrode. A potentiometer can be placed in the circuit, and the voltage of this galvanic cell can be measured. Further, if a slightly higher opposing voltage is impressed on the electrodes, the reactions will be reversed; if a slightly lower voltage is applied, the spontaneous reactions will again proceed. These are termed reversible cell reactions, and it is to this kind of cell reaction that the laws of thermodynamics can be applied.

The potential difference between the electrodes in our galvanic cell will be 1.10 v. Nothing, however, can yet be said about the magnitude of the charge in each half cell—only the difference has been measured. To overcome this difficulty, the convention has been universally adopted that a standard half cell is selected to which a potential of zero is assigned, independent of temperature. The half cell adopted is the hydrogen electrode, which consists of a platinized platinum electrode surrounded by flowing hydrogen at 1 atm pressure and dipping into an aqueous solution contain-

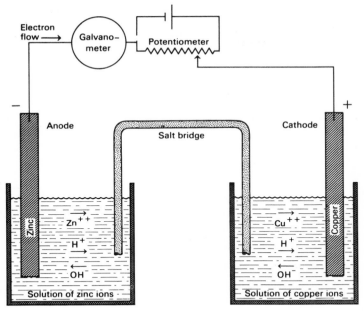

Fig. 7.1. Galvanic cell

ing hydrogen ions at unit activity. Therefore the potential difference of a cell involving a standard hydrogen electrode and some other standard half cell is assigned entirely to the latter and is known as the standard electrode potential. Tables that list standard electrode potentials are available (see Table 7.1). The values quoted are for the oxidation reactions at the particular electrodes. Therefore, these tables serve as a kind of reactivity index. They indicate the relative tendency of a metal to go into solution in acid environments with the liberation of hydrogen.

Sign Conventions. At this point it is appropriate to establish the sign conventions we have adopted, in order to avoid the regrettable confusion that sometimes arises. We shall consider that the electrode at which oxidation occurs is the anode and that the electrode at which reduction occurs is the cathode. Therefore, the corroding metal—that is, the less noble metal—is the anode. Since electrons are liberated at the corroding metal surface, the anode acquires a negative charge. The noncorroding metal—the more noble metal—is the cathode, which has a positive charge. At this electrode, hydrogen is evolved or ions are plated out. We shall further adopt the convention that a cell reaction is written with the anode on the left.

When the anode is connected externally to the cathode, electrons must

Table 7.1. Standard Electrode Potentials at 25 C (77.0 F) for Oxidation Reactions

Electrode	Electrode reaction	Potential, v
Li | Li$^+$	Li(s) = Li$^+$ + e	+3.024
K | K$^+$	K(s) = K$^+$ + e	+2.9241
Ca | Ca^{++}	Ca(s) = Ca^{++} + 2e	+2.763
Na | Na$^+$	Na(s) = Na$^+$ + e	+2.7146
Zn | Zn^{++}	Zn(s) = Zn^{++} + 2e	+0.7611
Fe | Fe^{++}	Fe(s) = Fe^{++} + 2e	+0.441
Cd | Cd^{++}	Cd(s) = Cd^{++} + 2e	+0.4021
Tl | Tl$^+$	Tl(s) = Tl$^+$ + e	+0.3385
Ni | Ni^{++}	Ni(s) = Ni^{++} + 2e	+0.236
Ag | AgI(s), I$^-$	Ag(s) + I$^-$ = AgI(s) + e	+0.1522
Sn | Sn^{++}	Sn(s) = Sn^{++} + 2e	+0.1406
Pb | Pb^{++}	Pb(s) = Pb^{++} + 2e	+0.1264
H$_2$ | H$^+$	H$_2$(g, 1 atm) = 2 H$^+$ + 2e	±0.0000
Ag | AgBr(s), Br$^-$	Ag(s) + Br$^-$ = AgBr(s) + e	−0.0711
Hg | Hg$_2$Br$_2$(s), Br$^-$	2 Hg(l) + 2 Br$^-$ = Hg$_2$Br$_2$(s) + 2e	−0.1385
Pt | Sn^{++}, Sn^{++++}	Sn^{++} = Sn^{++++} + 2e	−0.14
Ag | AgCl(s), Cl$^-$	Ag(s) + Cl$^-$ = AgCl(s) + e	−0.2225
Hg | Hg$_2$Cl$_2$(s), Cl$^-$	2 Hg(l) + 2 Cl$^-$ = Hg$_2$Cl$_2$ + 2e	−0.2680
Cu | Cu^{++}	Cu(s) = Cu^{++} + 2e	−0.3441
I$_2$ | I$^-$	2 I$^-$ = I$_2$(s) + 2e	−0.5362
Hg | Hg$_2$SO$_4$(s), SO$_4$$^{--}$	2 Hg(l) + SO$_4$$^{--}$ = Hg$_2$SO$_4$(s) + 2e	−0.6141
Pt | Fe^{++}, Fe^{+++}	Fe^{++} = Fe^{+++} + e	−0.7477
Ag | Ag$^+$	Ag(s) = Ag$^+$ + e	−0.7990
Br$_2$ | Br$^-$	2 Br$^-$ = Br$_2$(l) + 2e	−1.0659
Pt | Tl$^+$, Tl^{+++}	Tl$^+$ = Tl^{+++} + 2e	−1.211
Cl$_2$ | Cl$^-$	2 Cl$^-$ = Cl$_2$(g, 1 atm) + 2e	−1.3583
Pt | Ce^{+++}, Ce^{++++}	Ce^{+++} = Ce^{++++} + e	−1.55
Pt | Co^{++}, Co^{+++}	Co^{++} = Co^{+++} + e	−1.817

flow from the anode to the cathode since electrons are released at the anodic metal surface in the oxidation reaction and they are removed at the cathodic metal surface in the reduction reaction. Therefore electrons flow in the external circuit from anode to cathode. Flow of electricity, however, is popularly considered to be flow of "positive" current. Therefore, in the external circuit of our cell, "positive" current flows from cathode to anode. The circuit is completed by the internal circuit through the solution, in which positive ions move from anode to cathode and thus provide a positive charge to the cathode.

Cell Reaction. The reactions occuring in the cell shown in Fig. 7.1 are as follows: (*a*) Zn → Zn^{++} + 2e^- at the anode, where zinc dissolves (oxidation), and (*b*) Cu^{++} + 2e^- → Cu at the cathode, where copper plates out (reduction). Combining these reactions we have the following cell reaction: zinc + copper ions in sol. ⇌ zinc ions in sol. + copper plated out, which can be written as

$$Zn + Cu^{++} \rightleftharpoons Zn^{++} + Cu$$

Standard Cell Potential. E^0, the standard cell potential, is the sum of the standard half-cell potentials of the anode (oxidation reaction) and the cathode (reduction reaction). However, standard half-cell potentials, as listed in Table 7.1, are attributed a sign according to their *oxidation* potential. Therefore, the standard cell potential is determined by taking the *difference* in the half-cell potentials.

The driving force for the cell reaction is the excess chemical free energy of the reactants over the products. That is, a spontaneous reaction can occur when the products formed have a lower chemical free energy than the reactants. For standard conditions, the free-energy change, ΔF^0, is related to the standard cell potential, E^0, by

$$\Delta F^0 = -nFE^0 \tag{1}$$

where n is the number of electrons involved in the valence change of the particular ion, F is the Faraday equivalent (96,484 coulombs per gram equivalent weight of deposited ion), and E^0 is the standard cell potential. But the standard free-energy change, ΔF^0, is also related to the equilibrium constant of the reaction by the following relationship

$$\Delta F^0 = -RT \ln K \tag{2}$$

where R is the gas constant, T is the absolute temperature, and K is the equilibrium constant for unit activity of ions reacting (that is, the number of gram moles reacting times the activity coefficient equals one) and equals the activity of zinc ions in solution at equilibrium divided by the activity of copper ions in solution at equilibrium or $[Zn^{++}]/[Cu^{++}]$ at equilibrium.

Therefore, the standard cell potential is related to the equilibrium constant for the cell reaction as follows

$$E^0 = -(RT \ln K)/nF \tag{3}$$

The practical significance of this relationship can be shown by the following simple calculations to determine the concentration of the zinc ions and the copper ions in solution when the standard cell described above has attained equilibrium, that is when no further net chemical change occurs. From Eq 3

$$E^0 = (-2.303RT/nF) \log [(\text{activity zinc ions})/(\text{activity copper ions})]$$

where $n = 2$, $T = 273.15 + 25 = 298.15$ K, and $R = 8.315$ joules per degree. From Table 7.1, the value of E^0 for the cell reaction $Zn + Cu^{++} \rightarrow Zn^{++} + Cu$ is as follows:

$$E^0 = 0.7611 - (-0.3411) = 1.101$$

Therefore

$$(0.05915/2) \log (a_{Zn^{++}}/a_{Cu^{++}}) = 1.101$$

$$a_{Zn^{++}} = 10^{37} a_{Cu^{++}}$$

Thus, at equilibrium, the effective concentration of zinc ions in solution is greater than the effective concentration of cupric ions in solution by the astronomical factor of 10^{37}. In other words, when a strip of zinc and a strip of copper are immersed in an aqueous solution of copper sulphate, the zinc will continue to dissolve until all the cupric ions have been effectively removed from solution. The ratio of the concentrations of the products and reactants at equilibrium can be used as a qualitative measure of the extent to which a given cell reaction as written can occur or the tendency of one electrode to be anodic to the other, as written.

The standard state can be extended to include the general case of products and reactants at unspecified concentrations by the relationships:

$$E = E^0 - (RT/nF) \ln [(\text{activity of products})/(\text{activity of reactants})] \quad (4)$$

$$\Delta F = \Delta F^0 + (RT/nF) \ln [(\text{activity of products})/(\text{activity of reactants})] \quad (5)$$

The reader is advised to consult a standard text book on physical chemistry for a rigorous treatment of the subject.

In a similar manner to that described above a practical electromotive series or galvanic series of metals and alloys can be developed by immersing specimens in a particular industrial environment. Table 7.2 is a galvanic series for metals immersed in flowing sea water at 77 F. For purposes of practical convenience, a reference saturated calomel electrode, previously calibrated, was used as the cathode. The results show the relative tendency of the various samples to undergo the oxidation or anodic reaction.

Pourbaix Diagrams. Tremendous impetus to the study of corrosion problems by a thermodynamic approach has been gained through the works of M. J. N. Pourbaix, of the Belgian Center for the Study of Corrosion. Pourbaix diagrams, or diagrams of potential versus pH, are now available for practically all elements in equilibrium with aqueous solutions. Figure 7.2 shows a Pourbaix diagram for the study of corrosion of

Table 7.2. Galvanic Series in Sea Water at 77 F and Flowing at 13 ft/sec(a)

Metal	Steady potential (negative to standard calomel), v
Zinc	1.03
Aluminum 3003	0.94
Carbon steel	0.61
Gray iron	0.61
304 stainless steel (active)	0.53
Copper	0.36
Admiralty brass	0.29
70/30 copper-nickel (0.47% Fe)	0.25
Nickel 200	0.20
316 stainless steel (active)	0.18
Inconel alloy 600	0.17
Titanium	0.15
Silver	0.13
304 stainless steel (passive)	0.08
Monel alloy 400	0.08
316 stainless steel (passive)	0.05

(a) Data from F. L. LaQue, *Proc ASTM*, **51**, 495 (1951).

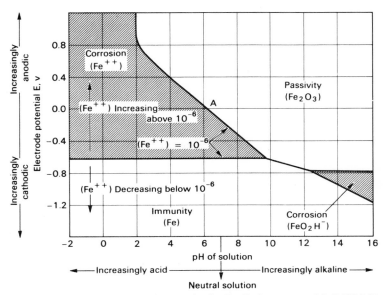

Fig. 7.2. *Simplified Pourbaix diagram for the Fe–H_2O system at 25 C (77.0 F) showing the domains of corrosion behavior. The symbol $[Fe^{++}]$ represents the equilibrium concentration of Fe^{++} ions in units of moles per liter of solution. From A. G. Guy and F. N. Rhines, Metal Treat. Drop Forging, **29**, 45 (1962)*

pure iron in contact with water at 25 C (77.0 F). It describes the corrosion behavior of iron under equilibrium conditions for given values of electrode potential and pH of the water.

Pourbaix has defined the condition for immunity to be the amount of reaction between the metal and its aqueous environment that would result in a concentration of metal ions in solution at equilibrium of less than 10^{-6} moles per liter—a very small amount. That is, when iron has reacted with an aqueous solution according to the reaction $Fe \rightarrow Fe^{++} + 2e^{-}$, corrosion is deemed to have occurred if the concentration of Fe^{++} ions at equilibrium is greater than 10^{-6} moles per liter. Using this criterion and the thermodynamic relationships previously developed, Pourbaix divides the diagram into regions of immunity, corrosion, and passivity for all possible reactions. These diagrams are most useful in that they show conditions for which a given corrosion reaction is or is not possible.

Polarization. The electrode reactions considered thus far have been thermodynamically reversible. However, many practical corrosion reactions involve irreversible phenomena. For instance, it is found that when hydrogen is deposited on a cathodic surface other than platinized platinum, a potential greater than the cell potential is required to reverse the reaction. This is termed hydrogen overvoltage, and the process is part of the general phenomenon of polarization. Polarization can also occur at the anode through the formation of a compound with some constituent of the electrolyte and its subsequent adherence to the anode as an impervious or passivating film. It is largely because of polarization effects such as hydrogen overvoltage and anodic passivity that most of the structural materials above hydrogen in Table 7.1 exhibit rates of corrosion lower than might be assumed from their standard potentials. The kinetics of a corrosion reaction are not defined in the thermodynamic treatment.

Sources of Corrosion Current

A number of sources of corrosion current have been implicit in the discussion thus far. A galvanic current arises from the presence of two different metals in the same solution. Another source of corrosion current arises from differences in composition within the same piece of material. Cold worked metal, for example, is anodic to the annealed structure. A corrosion current may be produced when the same kind of metal is present in two different solutions. In a differential aeration cell, for example, the aerated solution tends to make the metal cathodic toward the metal in contact with the deaerated solution. When design features permit concentration of solutions at crevices or in stagnant areas, a concentration corrosion cell arises, and the metal in contact with the concentrated solution of its ions is cathodic to the metal in contact with the dilute solution of its ions.

Corrosion in a Gaseous Environment

The electrochemical theory of corrosion can be extended to reactions in the gaseous phase, such as oxidation, sulfidation, and nitriding. Figure 7.3 depicts schematically concepts of corrosion in a gaseous environ-

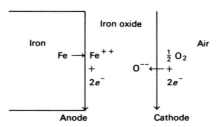

Fig. 7.3. Oxidation of iron at elevated temperature

ment for the case of oxidation of iron at elevated temperature. The cathode, at which reduction occurs, is considered to be the interface of the gas and the metal compound, and the anode, at which oxidation occurs, is considered to be the interface of the metal and the metal compound. For the case of oxidation of iron at elevated temperature, the following reactions occur: (a) $Fe \rightarrow Fe^{++} + 2e^-$, at the anode, and (b) $\frac{1}{2}O_2 + 2e^- \rightarrow O^{--}$, at the cathode. Subsequent diffusion of the mutually attracted ions results in formation of the scale.

The same principles employed in the study of corrosion of metals in aqueous mediums can be applied to the study of corrosion of metals in organic environments. Standard half-cell potentials can be developed in a similar manner for a specific organic solution.

The science of corrosion prevention and control is based upon a fundamental knowledge of electrochemical reactions and physical changes occurring at metal surfaces. The effect of surface condition on the kinetics of these reactions and perhaps on their initiation is not fully appreciated. The erratic behavior of chemical corrosion inhibitors is less perplexing when one realizes that the nature of the metal surface that they are intended to protect is itself relatively unknown. A fundamental approach to the study of metal surfaces, the formation of surface films, the adsorption of gases, and gas-metal reactions must complement the further development of basic electrochemical processes.

Chapter 8

Corrosion Resistance of Stainless Steels

Corrosion resistance is usually a major consideration in the selection of a particular grade of stainless steel for a given application. However, composition is not the only variable that affects behavior: heat treatment, surface condition, fabrication procedures may change the response of a given grade from relative inertness to unacceptable reactivity in a specific environment.

Basically, the corrosion resistance of all stainless steels rests upon the common factor of a high chromium content. Yet, as we can see from the electromotive series shown in Chapter 7, chromium occupies a position somewhat less noble than iron. When placed in an acid solution such as nitric acid, we should then expect chromium atoms to leave the metal surface and redissolve in the solution, liberating electrons.

However, it is well known that in spite of its position in the electromotive series, chromium is unattacked in nitric acid; it is also well known that steel containing at least 11% chromium is unattacked by nitric acid and by many other aqueous, organic, and gaseous environments that normally attack plain carbon steel. A clue to chromium's behavior is offered by the observation that chromium does not occur in nature as a native element (as gold and silver do), but as an oxidic mineral—frequently chromite, $FeO \cdot Cr_2O_3$. Nature, then, points the way to our most strategic alloys, the stainless steels and the higher chromium alloys, by showing us her tendency to produce chromium oxide. And the mechanism by which a stainless steel is inert in so many environments relates to the formation of this oxide through what is termed *passivation*.

The mechanism of passivation is not yet completely understood. But the current engineering appreciation of the process adequately explains most observable phenomena. Two hypotheses are generally put forward. One is that a monomolecular layer of chemisorbed oxygen on the surface of the steel effectively stifles any chemical reaction; the other is that a thin impervious oxide layer forms spontaneously on a chromium steel surface and hinders possible chemical reactions by preventing diffusion of reacting atoms across the passivating barrier. Although the subject of passivity has been intensively investigated for half a century and although the composition or the nature of the oxide film has not yet been completely established, it is profitable to think of the passivity of stainless steels in terms of a protective oxide layer that can be ruptured by mechanical and chemical methods, that can be breached with varying degrees of mobility by a number of ionic species, and that has the happy faculty of autocatalytic repair in oxidizing environments. The analogy with the theory of corrosion inhibitors is more than fortuitous. This concept of passsivity permits a degree of rationality to the very large number of recognized stainless grades.

The behavior of stainless steels in various environments is discussed below. In general, stainless steel castings exhibit comparable corrosion resistance to their wrought counterparts and will therefore not be discussed separately.

Atmospheric Corrosion

Rural and Uncontaminated Atmospheres. All grades of stainless steel are completely resistant to staining, rusting, pitting, scaling, or other surface deterioration even in tropical environments approaching 100% relative humidity.

Industrial Atmospheres. All classes of stainless steel resist staining, pitting, and corrosion in polluted urban atmospheres that do not contain chlorides. Some examples of this corrosion resistance, which were given in the 1961 report of the inspection task force of ASTM Committee A-10, "Report on Inspection of Corrosion-Resistant Steels in Architectural and Structural Applications," are summarized below:

1.　202 used on the service tower of the Inland Steel Building, Chicago, Ill., showed no signs of pitting or corrosion after annual cleaning at the end of two years' exposure. The side of the tower facing an alley was covered with an accumulation of dirt and oily smudge, but there was no sign of corrosion or pitting under this dirt.

2.　301 used on the exterior of the E. F. Hauserman Co. Building, Cleveland, Ohio, showed no evidence of any deterioration after ten years' exposure.

3.　302 used on the pilasters on the tower and mullions of the Empire State Building, New York, N. Y., showed practically no deterioration after 29 years' exposure. From a distance, despite adhering dirt, the stainless shines brightly, particularly on sunny days.

4.　430 used on the exterior of a building in Gateway Center, Pittsburgh, Pa., showed no signs of rusting or pitting after eight years.

5.　410 used on the exterior facings of the vaults of the Philadelphia Savings Fund Society Building, Philadelphia, Pa., showed no sign of pitting or corrosion after 18 years' exposure. (The stainless was wiped every three months with lemon oil to remove finger spots.)

In heavily polluted atmospheres, as in London, England, the use of 316 or the British Type "18–10–3" has been found necessary.

Marine Atmospheres. The passivating film on stainless steels is not impervious to chloride ions, and thus in environments containing chloride ions, all stainless steels are subject to staining and pitting. Table 8.1 gives

Table 8.1. Corrosion of Some Stainless Steels After Eight Years' Immersion in Sea Water(a,b)

AISI type	Weight loss, g/dm^2				Average depth of 20 deepest pits(c), mils				Deepest pit(d), mils				Type of corrosion attack
	1 yr	2 yr	4 yr	8 yr	1 yr	2 yr	4 yr	8 yr	1 yr	2 yr	4 yr	8 yr	
410	5.99	9.56	15.87	28.09	61 (11)	64 (11)	148	161	260 (P)	264 (P)	260 (P)	259 (P)	Localized, concentration cell pitting
302	2.93	4.43	7.06	10.89	70 (12)	74	107	140	261 (P)	238	286 (P)	236	Random pitting
316	1.18	0.65	0.54	4.08	44 (7)	52	48	154	245 (P)	82	93	245 (P)	Random pitting
321	2.32	3.44	6.55	10.22	64 (8)	120	175	193	270 (P)	206	273 (P)	272 (P)	Random pitting

(a) Data from U. S. Naval Research Laboratory
(b) Test location was 1½ miles from the shoreline near Fort Amados in the Panama Canal Zone.
(c) Numbers in parentheses are the total number of pits averaged when less than 20 were available.
(d) (P) indicates complete perforation.

corrosion data for some stainless steels after eight years' immersion in sea water, and Table 8.2 gives data for some steels after eight years' exposure to a seashore atmosphere. It can be seen that of these steels 316 is the most resistant to attack by the chloride ion.

High-Temperature Oxidizing Atmospheres Free of Sulfur, Halogens, Ammonia, and Hydrogen. In nonfluctuating-temperature service, the oxida-

Table 8.2. Corrosion of Some Stainless Steels After Eight Years' Exposure to a Seashore Atmosphere(a,b)

AISI type	Weight loss, g/dm^2				Type of corrosion attack
	1 yr	2 yr	4 yr	8 yr	
410	0.08	0.11	0.11	0.08	Some localized pitting
430	0.05	0.07	0.07	0.07	Some localized pitting
301	0.00	0.00	0.01	0.01	No visible attack
316	0.00	0.00	0.00	0.00	No visible attack
321	0.01	0.00	0.01	0.01	No visible attack

(a) Data from U. S. Naval Research Laboratory
(b) Test location was the roof of the Washington Hotel, 55 ft above sea level and 300 ft from the harbor at Cristobal, Panama Canal Zone.

tion resistance of stainless steels depends on the chromium content, as shown in Fig. 8.1. Steels with less than 18% chromium (ferritic grades) are limited to heat-resistant applications at temperatures below 1500 F. Those containing 18 to 20% chromium are useful at higher temperatures to

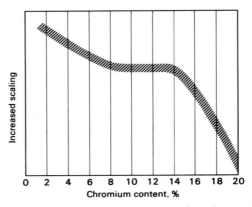

Fig. 8.1. Effect of chromium content on resistance of stainless steels to scaling at 1830 F

Table 8.3. Maximum Service Temperature Without Excessive Scaling for Stainless Steels(a,b)

AISI type	Nominal composition	Temp, F
Martensitic		
410	11.5–13.5 Cr	1250
420	12–14 Cr	1200
440	16–18 Cr	1400
Ferritic		
430	14–18 Cr	1550
446	23–27 Cr	2000
Austenitic		
302	17–19 Cr, 8–10 Ni	1650
303	17–19 Cr, 8–10 Ni	1600
304	18–20 Cr, 8–12 Ni	1650
309	22–24 Cr, 12–15 Ni	2000
310	25 Cr, 20 Ni	2000
316	16–18 Cr, 10–14 Ni, 2–3 Mo	1650
321	17–19 Cr, 9–12 Ni, Ti	1650
347	17–19 Cr, 9–13 Ni, Cb	1650

(a) Data from ASTM
(b) Based on a rate of oxidation of 10 mg per sq cm in 1000 hr

1800 F, while adequate resistance to scaling at temperatures up to 2000 F requires a chromium content of at least 25% (309, 310). The maximum service temperature based on a rate of oxidation of 10 mg per sq cm in 1000 hr is given in Table 8.3 for nonfluctuating-temperature service. The corrosion resistance of stainless steels in steam and oxidizing flue gases, compared with their corrosion resistance in air, is shown in Fig. 8.2.

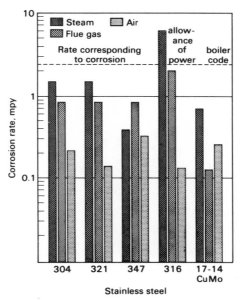

Fig. 8.2. *Comparative corrosion rates of stainless steels in steam at 1250 F, flue gas at 1200 to 1400 F, and air at 1400 F. Exposure time was 6950 hr for steam and flue gas and 1260 hr for air. From F. Eberle, F. G. Ely, and J. A. Dillon, Trans ASME,* **76**, *665 (1954)*

When fluctuating- or cycling-temperature conditions are involved, spalling and cracking of the scale may occur with a consequent high increase in the rate of oxidation. Although nickel increases the resistance to spalling (as shown in Fig. 8.3), a minimum chromium content of 25% appears to be essential.

A word of caution is necessary to users of stainless steels at high temperatures in oxidizing environments. The passivity of stainless steels breaks down in the presence of specific metal oxides with a resulting accelerated rate of attack that is termed *catastrophic oxidation*. Information available at present indicates that the 200 chromium-manganese-nickel series and the austenitic 18–8 series are susceptible to catastrophic

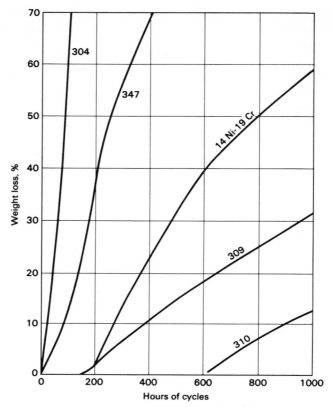

Fig. 8.3. Scaling resistance of some iron-chromium-nickel alloys in cycling-temperature conditions at 1800 F. Cycle consisted of 15 min in the furnace and 5 min in air. Sheet specimens 0.031 in. thick were exposed on both sides. From International Nickel Co. of Canada, Ltd.

oxidation in the presence of lead oxide at temperatures as low as 1300 F. Vanadium oxide, V_2O_5, found in fuel ash, is known to cause catastrophic failure of 310 and 309 at temperatures of 1900 F when water vapor is present. Molybdenum oxide, MoO_3, behaves in a similar manner. Although accelerated oxidation has been observed in high-molybdenum-bearing stainless steels, it is the molybdenum oxide vapor that catalyzes the oxidation reaction.

Although the mechanism of catastrophic oxidation is not fully explained, undoubtedly it has to do with the change in the normal spinel structure of the passivating film. The complex oxide usually formed has the general chemical form $Cr_2O_3 \cdot FeO$. Metal ions and oxygen ions can diffuse through this structure only with extreme difficulty. However in the presence of lead oxide, vanadium oxide, or molybdenum oxide, the structure of the passive film is changed to one that permits rapid diffusion of oxygen ions, and accelerated oxidation results.

High-Temperature Atmospheres Containing Ammonia. Since the use of ammonia is rapidly increasing with the expanding chemical fertilizer industry and as an industrial refrigerant, it is important to realize the limitations to the use of stainless steels in ammonia processing equipment. The synthesis of ammonia involves the reaction with a suitable catalyst of a mixture of hydrogen and nitrogen at pressures between 1500 and 15,000 psi and at temperatures around 1000 F. Under these conditions, most materials, including the stainless steels, are susceptible to nitriding, or the formation of a brittle nitride layer. Table 8.4 shows results obtained on

Table 8.4. Resistance of Stainless Steel to Attack in Two Types of Ammonia Converters and in a Plant Ammonia Line

	Depth of nitrided case, ipy			
	Ammonia converter		Plant ammonia line(a,b)	
AISI type	Haber-Bosch process(a,c)	Casale process(d,e)	Polished surface	Pre-oxidized surface
446	0.00112	0.015	0.1645	0.173
304	0.00059	0.014	0.0995	0.102
316	0.00047	0.006	>0.52	>0.5
309	0.00023	0.0032	0.0950	0.049
310	0.00014	0.0031	0.0535	0.007
80 Ni–20 Cr	No nitride phase	....	0.0074	0.004

(a) Data from J. J. Moran, J. R. Mihalisin, and E. N. Skinner, Corrosion, **17**, 115 (1961).
(b) Exposure time was 1540 hr; temperature was 935 F.
(c) Exposure time was 29,164 hr; temperature was 915 to 1024 F, average pressure was 5200 psi.
(d) Data from D. W. McDowell, Jr., Mat Protect, **1**, 19 (1962).
(e) Exposure time was 3 yr; temperature was 1000 F; average pressure was 11,000 psi.

samples of stainless steels that were exposed in the catalyst basket of two types of ammonia converters. The higher nitriding rates for the Casale process result from higher operating pressures. (Pressures used in the Casale process are between 9000 and 12,000 psi and are double those used in the Haber-Bosch process.)

Stainless steels are more rapidly attacked when the nitriding potential is higher. Table 8.4 shows the rate of nitriding obtained in a plant ammonia line. The composition of the gas was 99.1% ammonia and 0.9% inerts. Duplicate samples were exposed, one set having a prior oxidizing treatment at 1800 F for 15 min, to induce passivity. As in the tests with the Haber-Bosch process, the high-nickel-base alloy displayed better resistance to attack than the stainless steels. The behavior of the 316 samples was not fully explained.

High-Temperature Atmospheres Containing Sulfur or Its Compounds. Although the mechanism of sulfidation is similar to that of oxidation, greatly increased corrosion rates are encountered because sulfide scales are not generally as adherent or as protective as oxide scales. Further complications arise because many metal sulfide compounds have low melting points and fuse at high service temperatures. Sulfur vapor, hydrogen sulfide, and sulfur dioxide are the usually encountered constituents that attack most steels in high-temperature petrochemical processes. Increasing resistance of steels to sulfidation is obtained by increasing the chromium content.

Sulfur vapor readily attacks stainless steels at temperatures above the melting point of sulfur (832 F). The rate of corrosion in flowing sulfur vapor at 1060 F is shown for some ferritic and austenitic stainless steels in Table 8.5.

Table 8.5. Corrosion of Stainless Steels in Flowing Sulfur Vapor at 1060 F(a,b)

AISI type	Corrosion rate, mpy	AISI type	Corrosion rate, mpy	AISI type	Corrosion rate, mpy
446	10.8	309	22.3	316	31.1
314	16.9	304	27.0	430	44.6
310	18.9	302B	29.8	321	54.8

(a) Data from J. R. West, *Chem Eng*, **58**, 276 (1951).
(b) Data based on 1295-hr exposure.

Although 5% chromium steels are resistant to hydrogen sulfide at low partial pressures and at temperatures below 500 F, a minimum chromium content of about 17% is required under more severe conditions of temperature and concentration. The 200-series and the 18–8 austenitic stainless steels offer adequate resistance to corrosion in these conditions.

An example of the corrosion resistance of austenitic stainless steels in hot hydrogen sulfide is shown in the results of a test in which samples were exposed for 3840 hr at 615 F in the reactor effluent line ahead of the exchanger bank of Sinclair's Houston Straight Run Distillate Fuel Hydrodesulfurization Unit (see Fig. 8.4). The 37-degree API feed contained 0.60 wt % sulfur. The effluent stream, which was at 500 psi pressure, contained desulfurized product, hydrocarbon gases, about 50 mol % hydrogen, and an average of 0.45 mol % hydrogen sulfide. This investigation is particularly interesting because a 310 weld bead was deposited on three of the four series of samples. Welding did not increase the over-all

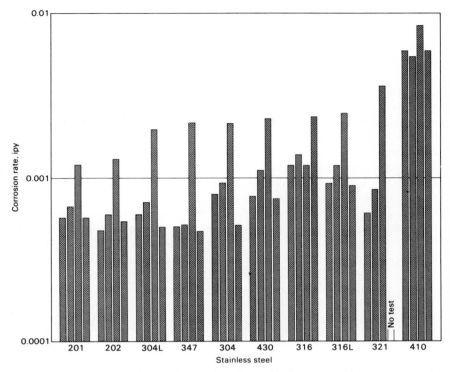

Fig. 8.4. Corrosion rates for stainless steels in 0.45 vol % hydrogen sulfide at 615 F. The as-received steel, which was in the solution annealed condition, was welded using 310 and then heated to 1200 F for 1 hr or to 1630 F for 16 hr. The first bar given for each alloy is for the as-welded condition; the second bar, the 1200 F heat treated condition; the third bar, the 1630 F heat treated condition; the fourth bar, the as-received condition. From F. J. Bruns, Corrosion, 17(5), 227t (1961)

corrosion rate appreciably, however, as can be seen by comparing the first and fourth bars for each alloy in Fig. 8.4.

As has been pointed out previously, unstabilized austenitic stainless steels in the as-welded condition are susceptible to intergranular corrosion because chromium carbides precipitate at the grain boundaries during cooling and there is localized chromium impoverishment at the grain boundaries. The over-all effect of grain-boundary carbide precipitation on the corrosion rate shown in the first bar for each alloy in Fig. 8.4 is slight, however, because the heat-affected zone in welding is small. A better measure of the effect of grain-boundary carbide precipitation on corrosion resistance is obtained by heating at 1200 F for 1 hr. Table 8.6

shows that this treatment resulted in general carbide precipitation at the grain boundaries in all the unstabilized medium-carbon austenitic grades (201, 202, 304, and 316). Corrosion data, however, showed only a slight increase, as can be seen by comparing the second and first bars for each alloy.

Heat treating at 1600 to 1650 F is sometimes used to produce homogeneous chromium diffusion and discrete carbide precipitation in unstabilized grades. The chromium impoverishment and continuous networks of grain-boundary carbide precipitation that occur in sensitization are thus avoided, and the steel is resistant to intergranular corrosion. Heating the alloys shown in Fig. 8.4 to 1630 F for 16 hr actually increased the corrosion rates, however, as shown in the third bar given for each alloy. Table 8.6 shows some of the microstructures produced by this "thermal stabilization" treatment. The manganese grades, whose corrosion rate was increased the least, show intergranular precipitation after the 1200 F treatment, but are in the solution annealed condition at 1630 F. The alloys whose corrosion rate was increased the most, 304L, 347, 316L, and 321, show no appreciable intergranular precipitation after the 1200 F treatment, but do show intergranular precipitation after the 1630 F treatment. The differences in corrosion rates are thus unexplained by the microstructures, but they do emphasize the fact that the corrosion resistance of stainless steels depends on heat treatment and fabrication vari-

Table 8.6. Microstructures of Heat Treated Stainless Steels Used in Hydrogen Sulfide Corrosion Test(a,b)

AISI type	Heat treatment	
	1200 F, 1 hr	1630 F, 16 hr
201, 202	Intergranular carbide precipitation network	Twinned hexagonal grains, no precipitated carbides, slow etching
304	Heavy carbide precipitation at grain boundaries and slip planes	Fine carbides within grains
316	Intergranular carbide precipitation	Larger grain size, intergranular carbide precipitation
304L	Light intergranular precipitation	Very large grains, intergranular precipitation
347	Discrete carbides in grain boundaries and in grains, stringered inclusion colonies	Larger grains, intergranular etching
321	Fine grained, slow etching, no carbide precipitation	Very large grains, discrete carbides at grain boundaries and in grains near surface

(a) From F. J. Bruns, *Corrosion*, **17** (5), 227t (1961).
(b) Oxalic acid electrolytic etch

ables. Although the maximum increase shown in Fig. 8.4 for the 1630 F treatment is only 0.0037 ipy, for more severe conditions the heat treatment would have a greater effect.

Information on the corrosion resistance of stainless steels to sulfur dioxide is lacking. However, it is reported that 316 developed no scale or tarnish at temperatures between 1100 and 1600 F when exposed for 24 hr to a series of mixtures of oxygen and sulfur dioxide varying from 100% oxygen to 100% sulfur dioxide. When water vapor is present, or when sulfurous acid can be formed, stainless steels are rapidly attacked.

High-Temperature Atmospheres Containing the Halogens and Their Compounds. The stainless steels are not generally useful for applications involving high-temperature halogen gases and their compounds. Corrosion rates at various temperatures in anhydrous chlorine, hydrogen

Table 8.7. Corrosion of Stainless Steels by Dry Chlorine and Hydrogen Chloride at High Temperatures(a)

AISI type	Corrosion rate, mpy										
	550 F	600 F	650 F	700 F	750 F	850 F	900 F	1050 F	1100 F	1150 F	1200 F
Chlorine											
304	30	60	120	· · ·	600	1200	· · ·	· · ·	· · ·	· · ·	· · ·
316	· · ·	30	60	· · ·	120	600	1200	· · ·	· · ·	· · ·	· · ·
Hydrogen chloride											
304	· · ·	· · ·	30	· · ·	60	120	· · ·	· · ·	600	· · ·	1200
309Cb	· · ·	· · ·	30	· · ·	60	120	· · ·	600	· · ·	1200	· · ·
316	· · ·	· · ·	· · ·	30, 60	· · ·	· · ·	120	· · ·	600	· · ·	1200

(a) Data from M. H. Brown, W. B. De Long, and J. R. Auld, *Ind Eng Chem*, **39**, 839 (1947).

chloride, fluorine, and hydrogen fluoride are given in Tables 8.7, 8.8, and 8.9. The rate of corrosion in fluorine is considerably higher than that in chlorine.

Corrosion in Liquid Environments

It is obviously impractical to discuss the corrosion resistance of all the stainless steels in all the various organic and inorganic solutions of acids, bases, and salts and in liquid-metal environments. A voluminous body of laboratory and field test data has been published by various stainless steel manufacturers and users, such as that shown in Tables 8.10 and 8.11. In the first instance, such data should be consulted as a guide. In the final analysis, complete confidence in the proper selection of a particular grade

Table 8.8. Corrosion of Stainless Steels by Dry Fluorine at High Temperatures(a)

AISI type	Corrosion rate, mpy								
	390 F	480 F	570 F	660 F	750 F	840 F	930 F	1080 F	1200 F
309Cb	Nil	Nil	900	5500	7900	· · ·	· · ·	· · ·	· · ·
310	Nil	Nil	370	410	6700	· · · ·	· · · ·	· · ·	· · ·
347	Nil	1700	2500	6100	9500	· · ·	· · ·	· · ·	· · ·
Nickel	· · ·	· · · ·	· · · ·	· · · ·	8	23	60	350	190

(a) From W. R. Meyers and W. B. DeLong, *Chem Eng Progr*, **44**, 359 (1948)

Table 8.9. Corrosion of Stainless Steels by Anhydrous Hydrogen Fluoride at High Temperatures(a)

AISI type	Corrosion rate, mpy		
	930 F	1020 F	1110 F
304	· · · ·	· · · ·	530
309Cb	230	1,680	6,600
310	480	395	12,000
347	7200	18,000	7,000
430	60	360	450

(a) Data from F. L. La Que and H. R. Copson, "Corrosion Resistance of Metals and Alloys," Reinhold Publishing Corp., New York, Second Edition, 1963, p. 432

of stainless for service in a specific environment can be achieved only by controlled tests under actual service conditions. Aeration, velocity, turbulence, and temperature, for example, can markedly affect corrosion resistance. In one instance, field data showed variations in average corrosion rates for gasoline (with various contaminants) by a factor of more than 100 with variations in temperature, aeration, and agitation. The reader is cautioned that the results of laboratory tests and field tests under simulated conditions can vary widely from actual results that are obtained in service.

Corrosion Failures

Because the corrosion resistance of stainless steels depends upon the passivating properties of a surface film, general corrosion is not suffered, except in instances of catastrophic oxidation, catastrophic sulfidation, or dissolution in nitric-hydrofluoric acid solutions. Stainless steels are, however, subject to localized forms of attack, which result in embrittlement or complete failure with seemingly little deterioration. Intergranular attack, stress-corrosion cracking, and pitting are the commercially important failure mechanisms of stainless steels.

Table 8.10. Corrosion Resistance of 302, 316, 430, and 410 in Various Solutions(a)

Organic Substances

Medium(b)	Corrosion resistance(c)			
	302	316	430	410
Acetone	u	u	u	s
Alkaform anesthesia	u	u	a	a
Benzol	u	u	u	u
Camphor	u	u	u	u
Carbon disulfide	u	u	..	..
Carbon tetrachloride	c	c	c	c
Carbon tetrachloride (vapors refluxed)	u	u	u	c
Coffee	c	c	c	c
Copal varnish	u	u	u	u
Ethyl alcohol	u	u	u	u
Ethyl chloride	u	u	u	u
Ethyl ether	u	u	u	u
Food pastes	u	u	u	u
Formaldehyde	c	c	c	c
Fruit juices	u	u	u	u
Furfural	u	u	..	..
Gasoline	u	u	u	u
Glue	c	c	c	c
Ink	c	c	c	c
Iodoform dressing	a	u	..	..
Methyl alcohol	u	u	u	u
Methyl chloride	u	u	..	..

Organic Substances (continued)

Medium(b)	Corrosion resistance(c)			
	302	316	430	410
Milk (fresh or sour)	u	u	u	u
Mustard	c	c	c	c
Naphtha	u	u	u	u
Oils (mineral and vegetable)	u	u	u	u
Paraffin (molten)	u	u	u	u
Paregoric cmpd	u	u	..	s
Pine tar oil	u	u	..	..
Quinine bisulfate	s	s	..	a
Quinine sulfate	u	u	..	s
Rosin (molten)	u	u	u	u
Soaps	u	u	u	u
Sodium salicylate	u	u	u	u
Soy bean oil	u	u	..	..
Tomato juice	c	c	c	c
Trichlorethylene	c	c	c	c
Tung oil	u	u	u	..
Vinegar (70 F)	c	c	c	c
Vinegar (plus 0.5% salt, 200 F)	c	c	c	c

Acids

Medium(b)	Corrosion resistance(c)			
	302	316	430	410
Acetic	c	c	c	c
Acetic vapor	c	c	..	a
Arsenic (150 F)	u	u	..	..

(continued on following page)

Table 8.10. Corrosion Resistance of 302, 316, 430, and 410 in Various Solutions(a) (Continued)

Acids (continued)

Medium(b)	Corrosion resistance(c)			
	302	316	430	410
Arsenic (225 F)	s	...	...	...
Arsenious	u	u	u	...
Benzoic	u	u	u	u
Boric	c	u	c	...
Butyric	u	u	u	...
Carbolic	c	c	a	a
Chloracetic	u	u	u	...
Chlorosulfonic (conc)	u	u	...	a
Chlorosulfonic (10%)	s	...	...	a
Chromic (50%)	a	a	a	...
Chromic	a	a	a	a
Chromic (plus 10% potassium ferricyanide)	...	...	...	...
Citric	u	u	...	s
Cresylic	u	u	...	s
Formic	a	c	...	a
Gallic	u	u	u	...
Hydrobromic	a	a	...	...
Hydrocyanic	u	u	a	a
Hydrochloric	a	a	a	a
Hydrofluoric	a	a	a	a
Lactic	u	u	u	s
Lactic plus salt	c	c	...	...
Malic	u	u	...	s
Molybdic	u	u	...	...

Acids (continued)

Medium(b)	Corrosion resistance(c)			
	302	316	430	410
Nitric (conc)	u	u	u	u
Nitric (conc plus 2% HCl)	u	...	a	a
Nitrous (conc)	u	u	u	s
Oleic	c	c	a	u
Oxalic	u	u	a	a
Phosphoric	u	u	a	...
Phosphoric (10%)	u	u	a	s
Picric (conc)	u	u	s	u
Pyrogallic (conc)	a	u	u	u
Pyroligneus (conc)	u	u	u	...
Stearic (conc)	u	u	...	u
Succinic (molten)	a	...	u	...
Sulfuric (conc)	u	u	a	a
Sulfuric (dil)	c	c	a	a
Sulfuric 15% (plus 2% potassium dichromate)	u	u	...	...
Sulfurous (conc)	c	u	s	s
Tannic (conc)	u	c	u	u
Tartaric (conc)	c	c	c	c
Uric (conc)	u	u	u	u

Salts

Medium(b)	Corrosion resistance(c)			
	302	316	430	410
Alum	c	c	...	c
Aluminum chloride	a	u	...	a
Aluminum fluoride	s	u	...	a

Salts (continued)

Salt				
Aluminum sulfate	u	u	…	s
Aluminum sulfate (sat. plus 1% sulfuric acid)	u	u	…	a
Aluminum sulfate (sat. plus 1% sodium carbonate)	u	u	…	u
Ammonium alum	u	u	u	…
Ammonium alum (sat.—slightly ammonical, 200 F)	u	u	…	a
Ammonium bromide	c	u	s	s
Ammonium carbonate	u	u	u	u
Ammonium chloride	c	c	s	s
Ammonium hydroxide	u	u	…	u
Ammonium monophosphate	u	u	u	…
Ammonium nitrate	u	u	u	u
Ammonium oxalate	u	u	u	u
Ammonium sulfate	u	u	u	s
Ammonium sulfate (plus 0.5% sulfuric acid)	u	u	…	a
Barium carbonate	u	u	u	…
Barium chloride	u	u	u	s
Barium hydrate	u	u	u	…
Bleaching powder	c	c	a	a
Bordeaux mixture	u	u	u	…
Calcium carbonate	u	u	u	u
Calcium chlorate	u	u	u	…
Calcium chloride	c	c	a	a
Calcium hypochlorite	a	c	a	a
Calcium hypochlorite made alkaline with NaOH	c	c	…	…

Salts (continued)

Salt					
Calcium hydroxide or oxide	u	u	u	u	u
Copper carbonate	u	u	u	u	u
Copper chloride	a	a	…	…	a
Copper cyanide	u	u	u	u	u
Copper nitrate	u	u	u	u	u
Copper sulfate (plus 2% sulfuric acid)	u	u	u	…	…
Copper sulfate	u	u	u	…	s
Creosote	a	a	c	…	…
Creosote (plus 3% salt)	a	a	…	…	a
Ferric chloride (10%)	a	u	u	a	a
Ferric nitrate	u	u	u	u	u
Ferrous sulfate	u	u	u	u	u
Ferric sulfate	u	u	u	u	u
Glauber's salt	u	u	u	u	…
Hydrogen peroxide	c	c	c	c	c
Lactic acid salts	u	u	u	u	…
Lead acetate	u	u	u	u	u
Magnesium carbonate	u	u	u	u	u
Magnesium chloride	c	c	c	a	a
Magnesium sulfate	u	u	u	u	s
Magnesium hydroxide	u	u	u	…	u
Magnesium nitrate	u	u	u	u	u
Mercurous nitrate	u	u	u	u	u
Mercuric chloride	c	u	c	a	a
Mercuric cyanide	u	u	u	u	s
Nickel nitrate	u	u	u	u	u
Phosphorous trichloride	u	u	u	u	…
Potassium bromide	u	u	u	…	s

(continued on following page)

Table 8.10. Corrosion Resistance of 302, 316, 430, and 410 in Various Solutions(a) (Continued)

Medium(b)	Corrosion resistance(c)			
	302	316	430	410
Salts (continued)				
Potassium carbonate	u	u	u	u
Potassium chloride	c	c	s	s
Potassium chlorate	u	u	u	…
Potassium cyanide	u	u	u	u
Potassium dichromate	u	u	u	u
Potassium ferricyanide	u	u	u	u
Potassium ferricyanide (boiling)	u	u	…	…
Potassium hypochlorite	a	c	a	a
Potassium iodide	u	u	…	…
Potassium iodide (sat. plus 0.1% sodium carbonate evaporated to dryness)	u	u	…	s
Potassium hydrate	u	u	u	u
Potassium nitrate	u	u	u	u
Potassium oxalate	u	u	u	u
Potassium permanganate	u	u	u	…
Potassium sulfate	u	u	u	u
Silver bromide	u	u	u	u
Silver nitrate	u	u	u	u
Silver cyanide	u	u	u	…
Sodium acetate	u	u	…	…
Sodium bicarbonate	u	u	u	…
Sodium bichromate	u	u	u	…
Sodium bisulfate	u	u	…	…

Medium(b)	Corrosion resistance(c)			
	302	316	430	410
Salts (continued)				
Sodium borate	u	u	u	…
Sodium bromide	u	u	…	s
Sodium carbonate (10%)	u	u	u	u
Sodium carbonate (50%)	u	u	u	…
Sodium chlorate (10%)	u	u	u	…
Sodium chlorate (25%)	u	u	u	…
Sodium chloride	c	c	…	…
Sodium chloride (2% aerated)	u	u	s	…
Sodium citrate	u	u	u	u
Sodium fluoride	s	…	…	…
Sodium hydroxide	u	u	u	u
Sodium hypochlorite (Dakin's solution)	c	c	a	a
Sodium hypochlorite (sat.— slightly alkaline, 200 F)	u	u	…	s
Sodium lactate	u	u	…	u
Sodium nitrate	u	u	u	u
Sodium nitrite	u	u	…	u
Sodium peroxide (212 F)	u	u	u	…
Sodium phosphate	u	u	…	…
Sodium sulfate	u	u	u	u
Sodium sulfide	u	u	u	u
Sodium sulfite	u	u	u	u
Sodium thiosulfate (plus 4% potassium meta bisulfate)	u	u	u	u

Salts (continued)

Sodium thiosulfate 20% plus acetic acid 20%	c	c	c	a
Soda ash (10%, 200 F)	u	u	u	u
Soda ash (50%, 200 F)	u	u	u	a
Stannic chloride	a	a	…	a
Stannous chloride	s	…	a	a
Sulfur (molten, 500 F)	u	u	u	…
Sulfur chloride	s	…	…	…
Titanium tetrachloride	u	…	…	a
Zinc chloride	a	s	…	a
Zinc sulfate	u	u	u	u

Miscellaneous

Aluminum (molten)	a	a	a	…
Ammonia	u	u	u	…
Baking oven gases	u	u	u	u
Beer	u	u	u	u
Bromine	a	a	a	a
Bromine water	a	a	a	a
Cadmium (molten)	a	a	…	…
Carbonated beverages	u	u	u	u
Chlorine (wet and dry)	a	a	a	a
Cider	u	u	u	u
Copper sulfate electroplating solution	u	u	…	…
Copper cyanide electroplating solution	u	u	…	…

Miscellaneous (continued)

Glycerin	u	u	u	u
Gold cyanide electroplating solution	u	u	u	u
Hydrogen sulfide (400 F)	c	c	c	…
Iodine	a	a	a	a
Lead (molten)	a	a	…	a
Linseed oil	u	u	…	s
Lysol	c	c	a	a
Meats	u	u	…	…
Mercury	u	u	c	…
Mine water	c	c	c	c
Nickel sulfate electroplating solution	u	u	…	…
Sauerkraut brine	a	a	…	…
Sea water	c	c	c	a
Silver cyanide electroplating solution	u	u	…	…
Steam and air (refluxed)	u	u	s	s
Steam, CO_2, and air	u	u	s	s
Steam, SO_2, CO_2, and air	s	s	c	s
Sulfur dioxide	c	c	s	…
Syrup	u	u	u	u
Vegetable juices	u	u	u	u
Water	u	u	u	u
X-ray developing solution	c	c	…	…
Zinc (molten)	a	a	a	a

(a) Data from Allegheny Ludlum Steel Corp.

(b) Except where stated, all tests were conducted on chemically pure materials, saturated solutions of salts, at room temperature.

(c) Code used is as follows: u indicates that the alloy was unaffected; s indicates that the alloy was slightly attacked; a indicates that the alloy was attacked; c indicates that complete service conditions are required for assessment.

Table 8.11. Corrosion of Stainless Steels by Liquid Metals(a)

Molten metal	Container metal, AISI type	Resistance of container metal
Lithium	302, 303, 304, 316, 347, 446	Resistant to 600 F
Magnesium	All types	Attacked at 1204 F
Thallium	All types	Resistant to 1200 F
Cadmium	All types	Poor resistance from its melting point to 1200 F
Zinc	All types	Poor at 930 F
Antimony	All types	Poor resistance to antimony. Resistant to cadmium alloys with over 50% antimony to 185 F above liquidus
Mercury	304	20 mpy at 1210 F
	310	47 mpy at 1210 F
	446	Good to 1020 F
Aluminum	All types	Embrittlement penetration at melting point of aluminum (1220 F)
Gallium	347, 430	Satisfactory to 390 F
	All types	Severe alloying at 1110 F
Indium	304	Superficial attack at 1200 F
Bismuth	347	Minor attack up to 1500 F
	446	Better then austenitic grades from 900 to 2220 F
	All types	Good up to 500 F
Bismuth-lead alloy (Eutectic 55.5% Bi, 44.5% Pb)	304	Gained weight at 900 F; 7.2 mpy at 1200 F
	317	1.8 mpy at 1200 F
	310	0.2 mpy at 900 F; gained weight at 1200 F
	430	Good to 1000 F
Bismuth-lead-tin alloy (Eutectic 52% Bi, 32% Pb, 16% Sn)	304	2.4 mpy at 1200 F
	317	3.9 mpy at 1200 F
	310	7.8 mpy at 1200 F
	446	Gained weight at 1200 F
Tin	All types	Suited to short-time use at melting point of tin (450 F)

(a) From R. N. Lyon, "Liquid-Metals Handbook," U. S. Government Printing Office, Washington, Second Edition, 1952, NAVEXOS P-733 (Rev.)

Intergranular Attack. Austenitic stainless steels of the 200 and 300 series, when heated in the range 800 to 1600 F and slowly cooled, become susceptible to failure by intergranular corrosion (Fig. 8.5). The commonly held theory of chromium impoverishment is adequate for our purposes: slow cooling from the sensitizing temperature range permits the precipitation of a chromium-rich carbide at the grain boundaries. The adjacent areas, decreased in chromium, become anodic sites in an electrochemical corrosion cell in acidic environments.

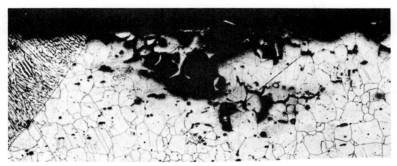

Fig. 8.5. Intergranular corrosion in heat-affected zone of welded 18–8 austenitic stainless steel. 100 ×. From A. Hanson and J. Gordon Parr, "The Engineer's Guide to Steel," Addison-Wesley, 1965

During the 35 years since this kind of failure was first diagnosed, the following preventive measures, which depend on avoiding the precipitation of carbides in the austenite grain boundaries, have been developed:

1. Reduction of carbon content in some grades (the extra-low-carbon grades) to a maximum of 0.03%.

2. Additions of titanium, as in 321, and columbium, as in 347. Titanium and columbium carbides will preferentially form a dispersed phase on cooling from annealing temperatures.

As pointed out in Chapter 4, sensitization, or susceptibility to intergranular corrosion, can be removed by reheating to the temperature range 1800 to 2000 F and rapidly cooling from this temperature.

The following tests are used for measuring the susceptibility to intergranular corrosion of as-received or heat treated austenitic stainless steels:

1. Huey nitric acid test (1930) according to ASTM Spec. A262-55T. A sample is boiled in 65% nitric acid for five 48-hr periods, each period in a fresh solution. Although this is generally a weight-loss determination, intergranular attack also can be observed.

2. Strauss copper sulfate test (1931) according to ASTM Spec. A393-55T. The test consists of boiling a sample for 72 hr in an acidified copper sulfate solution containing 100 g of $CuSO_4 \cdot 5H_2O$, and 100 ml of concentrated H_2SO_4 per 1000 ml of water. The samples are then bent and examined for cracks at low magnification. The test is used to verify as-received extra-low-carbon grades, to qualify welding procedures, and to approve heat treatment procedures.

3. Nitric-hydrofluoric acid test (not yet standardized). The solution consists of 20% HNO_3 and 4% HF heated to 160 F. The exposure time may vary from four 30-min periods to several weeks.

Intergranular corrosion of ferritic stainless steels also has been known since the early 1930's, but little investigation has been carried out on the problem. The laboratory tests used to detect susceptibility are the same as those for austenitic types. However, the behavior of ferritic stainless steels differs markedly in the following ways:

1.   Rapid cooling of ferritic steels from the range 1800 to 2000 F causes sensitization; slow cooling from this range prevents it.

2.   Reheating and slow cooling from the range 1200 to 1500 F immunizes ferritic steels against intergranular corrosion.

3.   Susceptibility of ferritic steels cannot be prevented with as little as 0.005% carbon, unless the nitrogen content is less than 0.01%.

4.   Susceptibility of ferritic steels increases with increasing chromium content.

Stress-Corrosion Cracking.   Since stress-corrosion cracking was first recognized about 25 years ago, interest and intensity of investigation have not waned.   Perhaps this is due to the potentially catastrophic nature of the failure and to the serious materials gap that is created each time a stainless steel is found to be susceptible to stress-corrosion cracking in a new specific environment. Regrettably, the mechanism of stress-corrosion cracking still awaits a precise explanation.

Stress-corrosion cracking is the brittle fracture of an alloy, exposed to a specific corroding medium, at low tensile stress levels with respect to the design strength of the alloy.   Although a tensile stress must be present, it may be residual or applied, or a combination of these. The time to failure in each environment is unpredictable: it depends upon the total stress, the temperature, and the effective concentration of the aggressive ionic species.   Only pure metals are immune to stress-corrosion cracking, and for all other metals and alloys there exists a set of conditions for which failure may occur by stress-corrosion cracking.   The fracture is generally at right angles to the direction of stress.   It is characteristic of this failure mechanism that a specific aggressive anion can be identified with a particular class of alloys.

The stress-corrosion cracking of austenitic stainless steels is predominantly transgranular.   An example of transgranular stress-corrosion cracking is shown in Fig. 8.6.   The halogen ions, particularly the chloride ion, are associated with stress-corrosion cracking of austenitic stainless steels under stress in aqueous solutions.   Table 8.12 shows chloride solutions known to cause stress-corrosion cracking in austenitic stainless steels. Obviously it is not practical to suggest that a minimum concentration of chlorides is necessary to produce stress-corrosion cracking.   Failures have occurred in solutions with an average chloride content of one part per million, but it is difficult to evaluate the extent of localized concentration of the chlorides.   An analysis of case histories reveals that the time to

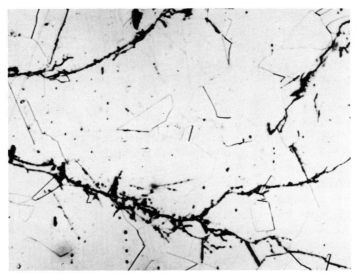

Fig. 8.6. Transgranular stress-corrosion cracking in 304 stainless steel due to the presence of the chloride ion. 250 ×. From A. Hanson and J. Gordon Parr, "The Engineer's Guide to Steel," Addison-Wesley, 1965

Table 8.12. Chloride Solutions That Cause Stress-Corrosion Cracking of Austenitic Stainless Steels(a)

Salt	Concentration, wt %	Temp, F
Ammonium chloride	30	Boiling
Calcium chloride	37	Boiling
Cobalt chloride	Saturated	212
Lithium chloride	30	Boiling
Magnesium chloride	40 (pH 4)	220
Magnesium chloride	60 (pH 4.4)	240
Magnesium chloride	42	310
Mercuric chloride	10	Boiling
Sodium chloride	Saturated	212
Zinc chloride	54	Boiling

(a) Data from International Nickel Co. of Canada, Ltd.

failure varies from a few days to several years, and therefore accelerated laboratory tests are recommended for new applications of austenitic stainless steels under stress in corrosive solutions.

Stress-corrosion cracking in austenitic stainless steels can be summarized as follows:

1.   An incubation period is required before the cracks can be detected.

2.   Cracks initiate at anodic sites on a surface stressed in tension. Dissolution of metal must occur at the crack front.

3.   Dissolved oxygen aggravates the situation.

4.   Low pH solutions are more aggressive than high pH solutions.

5.   A liquid H_2O phase must be present.

6.   A minimum or threshold stress is required, although a definition of the value remains obscure.

7.   An electrochemical reaction is the basic process, but the relative roles of stress and of corrosion are not yet established.

8.   A significant suggestion is that stress-corrosion cracking occurs only in ductile materials. This leads to entertaining speculations about the relative effects of corrosion products on dislocation movements in the crystal lattice and on the surface free energy of the metal.

Intergranular stress-corrosion cracking has been reported in ferritic stainless steels, but the matter has not been dealt with separately from intergranular corrosion failures.

Stress-corrosion cracking has been reported in 410 (a martensitic stainless steel), when tempered at 650 F to a hardness of Rockwell C 36 to 42, in high-purity, high-temperature water. Failure did not occur in specimens tempered at 1125 to 1350 F to a hardness of Rockwell C 26. Stress-corrosion cracking has also occurred in 410 in sour gas service—the familiar sulfide stress cracking, as shown in Fig. 8.7. However, in both cases intergranular fracture paths occurred along the prior austenite grain boundaries. Stress-corrosion cracking occurs through the anodic dissolu-

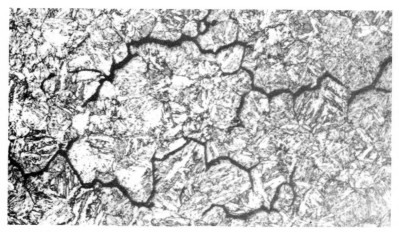

Fig. 8.7. Stress-corrosion cracking in 410 stainless steel in sour-gas service.
200×

tion of yielding metal at an advancing crack tip, where there is a concentration or pileup of dislocations. This can occur only in materials that are intrinsically ductile. The martensitic stainless steels, susceptible to intergranular cracking in hydrogen sulfide environments, do not display sufficient ductility to permit this sort of cracking mechanism, and it seems more reasonable to relate the failure to hydrogen embrittlement.

Stress-corrosion cracking has also been reported in precipitation-hardening martensitic and semi-austenitic stainless steels in high-purity, high-temperature steam. In accordance with the general theory of stress-corrosion cracking, the application of stainless steels heat-treated to high strength levels should be approached with caution in new environments for which the susceptibility to stress-corrosion cracking has not been assessed.

Pitting. Metals depending on a passive film for corrosion protection are susceptible to a severe form of attack known as pitting. Small localized areas may suffer destruction of the passivating film and become anodic to the rest of the surface. The resulting "corrosion cells" cause the formation of rapidly penetrating pits that lead to complete perforation.

Pitting of the stainless steels is associated with the presence of halogen ions, notably the chloride ions, in aqueous solutions. Although some improvement in resistance to pitting can be achieved through alloying additions, principally of molybdenum and additional chromium, complete immunity to pitting has not been achieved either by alloying or by heat treatment procedures.

The following procedures offer improved resistance to pitting attack:

1. Agitation, frequent washing, and full exposure to avoid concentration of halogen ions.

2. Vigorous aeration to prevent formation of oxygen concentration cells. Oxygen concentration should be increased, or oxygen should be eliminated.

3. Avoidance of low pH solutions. Alkaline chloride solutions cause less pitting or none at all.

4. Use of high-chromium, high-molybdenum alloys.

5. Use of inhibitors such as nitrates or chromates.

6. Operation at lowest possible temperature.

7. Encouragement of an anodic condition in the steel by anodic protection.

Appendix A
Measurement of Mechanical Properties

Mechanical properties are frequently referred to in this book. Here we shall define the terms we have used, describe the way in which the properties are measured, and mention some limitations of their applicability.

Tensile Properties

The most frequently used strength properties are those that are determined in the tension test. A straight sample is pulled in tension, and appropriate measurements are made. Although it is not always necessary to plot a curve of the force applied versus the length change suffered by the sample, such a curve will help us to understand the parameters we wish to define.

The *stress* applied to the sample is calculated by dividing the measured load by the original cross-sectional area of the sample. The *strain* is obtained by dividing the increase in length by the initial length of an arbitrarily chosen *gage length*. The gage length is (in North America) usually 2 in., but sometimes 8 in.

If the load and gage length are continuously measured while the sample is pulled, and if the stress and strain are computed from the measurements and plotted, a curve such as that shown in Fig. A.1 is obtained: this is the engineering stress-strain curve. The most important parts of the curve are (*a*) OA, the initial straight portion, (*b*) point A, the point at which the initial linearity disappears, and (*c*) point B, the point at which the stress is maximum.

Elastic Modulus. During the course of the test incorporated by OA, the sample behaves elastically. Were the load to be removed, the sample would regain its original dimensions. The slope of the line OA, measured by dividing OC by OD, gives us what is called Young's modulus of the material: a measure of the amount of elastic deflection suffered under a given load:

$$\text{Young's modulus } E = \text{stress/strain} = \text{OC/OD}$$

Materials with a high value of Young's modulus deflect a smaller amount, under a given load, than materials with a low value. Generally,

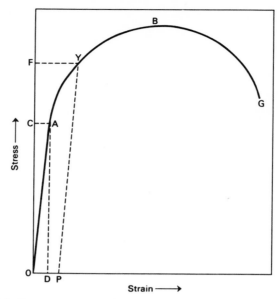

Fig. A.1. Stress-strain curve. Point P represents a plastic extension of 0.2%

the soft metals have low values of Young's modulus, while hard metals with high melting points have high values. Iron and its alloys have a value of about 30 million psi (compared with tungsten with 50 million and lead with 2 million). The figure is not changed by alloying, but, because of an effect of preferred orientation, it may be changed by working the metal. However, this change in most circumstances is not great, and we may assume that Young's modulus for the stainless steels in any condition is between 28 and 30 million psi.

Yield Stress.   The definition of yield stress has to be arbitrary, and our intention in measuring it is to state a value of stress at which the material changes from elastic to plastic behavior. In the curve of Fig. A.1, the metal will begin to behave plastically at loads greater than that at (approximately) A: if the load is removed after higher values have been reached, the sample will not return to its original shape—it will have suffered plastic deformation.

Precise measurement of the stress at A is difficult. Some materials (most notably the as-rolled mild steels) show a marked *yield extension* in the tension test, as Fig. A.2 illustrates. The stainless steels, however, show a curve of which Fig. A.1 is typical. In order to standardize some figure that may be called a *yield stress* most specifying bodies call for what is known as the *0.2% offset*. That is, rather than try to determine exactly where

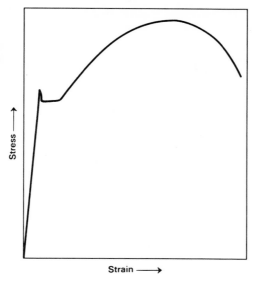

Fig. A.2. Stress-strain curve typical of mild steel

point A lies, the yield stress is taken as the stress at which the sample has suffered a permanent strain of 0.2%. Such a stress is computed by drawing a line parallel to OA, displaced along the horizontal axis by a value of strain equal to 0.2%: this is the line PY in Fig. A.1. The stress at Y (F in Fig. A.1) is the *yield stress*. Strictly speaking we should always refer to this as the 0.2% offset yield stress, because there are other ways of defining a yield stress—which we will not describe here.

Ultimate Tensile Stress. The stress at which the sample breaks corresponds to that at point G in Fig. A.1. However, the drop in stress compared with that at point B, is because during plastic yielding (from point A on) the sample *necks*: it thins locally, so that the cross section bearing the load becomes progressively smaller. From A to B this thinning is accommodated by the effect of *work hardening*: the material is becoming stronger. A maximum load during the test is reached at point B, and the value of this load divided by the original cross-sectional area of the sample is known as the ultimate tensile strength of the material.

The discerning reader will realize at once that the value of the ultimate tensile strength is not really so "ultimate," because it is based upon the original cross-sectional area—not the area at the moment at which this maximum occurs—and it is not the breaking stress. This is not the occasion to embark upon the topic of *true stress* (or for that matter, *true strain*). The simple fact is that for convenience the ultimate tensile strength is defined as the maximum load sustained in the tension test divided by the original cross-sectional area.

A further point of interest lies in the fact that the values of yield and ultimate strength pertain to a simple uniaxial load. Relating these values to a system in which complex stresses are involved is not easy: one usually relies on experience, and, indeed, the application of the results of the tension test to practical circumstances inevitably involves the interplay of test measurements and field experience. This is one reason, of course, why designs based upon the yield stress call for a *safety factor*. The subject of the relationship between yield stress as measured in the tension test and yielding under complex loading is dealt with in texts on the mechanics of materials.

Ductility. Two measurements of ductility—the amount of plastic deformation a material will endure prior to fracture—are usually made during the tension test: elongation and reduction of area.

To measure elongation, two marks, usually 2 in. apart (sometimes 8 in. apart) are made on the tensile specimen. After the test, the broken pieces of the sample are fitted together, and the distance between the marks is measured. Elongation is then calculated as

$$\frac{\text{length between marks after fracture minus original length}}{\text{original length}} \times 100\%$$

The exact meaning of this parameter is elusive. Indeed, the suggestion has been made that "elongation" has no meaning at all. However, as a measure of ductility (one dare not be more specific) it offers an easily obtained figure that can be compared with figures for other materials and related to service performance.

The value of elongation depends upon the gage length selected, because plastic extension is a localized condition. It is usually safe to assume that elongation figures quoted on the North American continent relate to a 2-in. gage length, unless otherwise indicated.

Reduction of area is probably a more meaningful value, but, although it is often specified, it is not so frequently used as the elongation figure. Reduction in area is defined as

$$\frac{\text{cross-sectional area after fracture minus original area}}{\text{original area}} \times 100\%$$

Hardness

Hardness can be defined in many ways, but the most common is that it is a measure of a material's resistance to indentation, and most hardness tests involve making an indentation under a measured load. The size of the indentation is then obtained, and the hardness figure is derived by dividing the load by some function of the area of the indentation.

The most common hardness tests used in North America are the Brinell and the Rockwell. The Rockwell has the advantage of being a simpler test to run: the size of the indentation is assessed by the indentor itself, and a hardness figure is directly read on the dial of the machine. However, it has the disadvantage of involving more than one scale. For example, for scale B, a load of 100 kg bearing upon a 1/16-in. spherical indentor is used; for scale C a load of 150 kg on a diamond-cone indentor is used.

Creep Properties

The tension test is performed in a few minutes. But we may wish to appraise the behavior of a material when it is subjected to a load for prolonged periods of time. Most commercial metals will, at room temperature, sustain for long periods of time the loads indicated by the quick tension test. However, at elevated temperature the length of time for which a material is under load is a major factor in determining what we may wish to call its strength. And, of course, depending upon the application of the material, short- or long-term service may be called for.

In order to assess long-term strength, creep tests can be run, in which a sample is stressed for long periods at elevated temperature. Two principal sorts of information can be obtained from the creep test: first, the stress to rupture at a given temperature for a given time of testing; second, the stress required at a given temperature to produce a specified amount of strain.

There is a temptation to extrapolate creep data: one may wish to know for how many years a piece of metal will give satisfactory service at (let us say) 1200 F. Naturally, there is limited enthusiasm to run a test over several years before putting the material in service. So a test may be run at a series of higher temperatures, or with higher loads, and an attempt is then made to extrapolate the data to lower values of temperature or stress. The extrapolation is not always reliable.

Fatigue Properties

The tension test involves the single application of a load. In service a metal may be subjected to the repeated application of a load. All metals will fail under repeated tensile loading at a stress level considerably lower than that which is sustained during a single application. Under these circumstances the metal fails by what is known as *fatigue*—one of the most common sources of metal failure.

There is a rule of thumb that a metal's fatigue limit (or endurance limit) is half of its ultimate tensile strength. It should be emphasized that this is usually the best that one may expect: more often than not, the fatigue limit is much lower. While the fatigue limit of a metal will increase as its tensile strength increases, a susceptibility to fatigue failure is encouraged by stress concentrations in design and by the action of corrosive environments. In fact, the designer of alloys can do very much less to avoid fatigue failures than can the designer of the structure in which the metal is to be incorporated.

Notch Ductility

Metals that do not have a face-centered cubic structure suffer a ductile-brittle transition at a temperature that depends upon the way in which ductility is assessed. In simple tension, for example, mild steel loses its ductility at about −300 F. But if ductility is assessed by the increasingly common impact test, then, under the influence of a notch and the application of a bending load, the ductile-brittle transition temperature is around room temperature.

The notch ductility of a material is usually appraised by the impact test, in which a notched sample is subject to a blow from a swinging hammer. The amount of energy absorbed by the sample during fracture is easily computed if the mass of the hammer is known and if the heights from which it was released and to which it swings after breaking the sample are measured. Although the testing principle is the same, the shape of the sample, its notch, and the height from which the hammer is released are different in the two most common impact tests, the Izod and the Charpy.

The transition temperature, as measured by these tests, is usually determined by running a series of tests at decreasing temperatures and finding at which temperature the absorbed energy drops to a stated value. Alternatively the transition temperature can be defined in terms of a change in character of the fracture of the samples.

It is important to appreciate that the purpose of the impact test is not to appraise the performance of a material under impact loads in service. Nor will the measured transition temperature be a temperature above which the material can be safely used. The test and the way in which the transition temperature are defined have been to some extent standardized so that we may have a consistent means of comparison: but the values obtained in the test cannot be directly applied to a structural design.

The topic of notch ductility is complex, and the reader who has to tangle with it is advised to read an authoritative text on the subject. We simply mention the subject here so that he may know (if he does not already) what is meant by the *impact values* quoted in the text of this book and—we hope—so that he may at least be cautious in his use of impact data.

Appendix B
Physical Properties of Stainless Steels

AISI Type	Melting range, F	Density, (32–212 F), lb/in.³	Specific heat (32–212 F), Btu/°F/lb	Thermal conductivity, Btu/ft²/hr/°F/ft		Mean coefficient of thermal expansion, in./in./°F $\times 10^{-6}$		Electrical properties		
								Magnetic permeability(a)	Resistivity, microohm-cm	
				212 F	932 F	68–212 F	68 F to temperature indicated		68 F	1200 F
Austenitic										
201	....	0.28	0.12	9.4	....	9.2	11.3 (1600 F)	1.02 max	69.0	....
202	....	0.28	0.12	9.4	....	9.4	10.9 (1600 F)	1.02 max	69.0	....
301	2550–2590	0.29	0.12	9.4	12.4	9.2	11.0 (1600 F)	1.02	72.0	116.0
302	2550–2590	0.29	0.12	9.4	12.4	9.2	11.0 (1600 F)	1.02	72.0	116.0
304	2550–2650	0.29	0.12	9.4	12.4	9.2	11.0 (1600 F)	1.02	72.0	116.0
304L	2550–2650	0.29	0.12	9.4	12.4	9.2	11.0 (1600 F)	1.02	72.0	116.0
309	2550–2650	0.29	0.12	9.0	10.8	8.7	10.9 (2100 F)	1.02	78.0	114.8
310	2550–2650	0.29	0.12	8.0	10.8	8.0	10.9 (2100 F)	1.01	78.0	....
316	2500–2550	0.29	0.12	9.4	12.4	9.2	10.7 (1600 F)	1.02	74.0	116.0
316L	2550–2650	0.29	0.12	9.4	12.4	9.2	10.7 (1600 F)	1.02	72.0	116.0
317	2500–2550	0.29	0.12	9.4	....	9.2	10.7 (1600 F)	1.02	79.0	....
347	2550–2600	0.29	0.12	9.3	12.8	9.2	10.7 (1600 F)	1.02	73.0	....
Martensitic										
410	2700–2790	0.28	0.11	14.4	16.6	5.5	6.4 (1300 F)	Magnetic	57.0	108.7
431	2550–2650	0.28	0.11	11.7	....	5.5	6.5 (1050 F)	Magnetic	72.0	....
440A	2500–2750	0.28	0.11	14.0	....	5.8	6.2 (1600 F)	Magnetic	60.0	....

(continued on next page)

Appendix B (Continued)

AISI Type	Melting range, F	Density, (32–212 F), lb/in.³	Specific heat, Btu/°F/lb	Thermal conductivity, Btu/ft²/hr/°F/ft		Mean coefficient of thermal expansion, in./in./°F × 10⁻⁶		Magnetic permeability(a)	Electrical properties, Resistivity, microhm-cm	
				212 F	932 F	68–212 F	68 F to temperature indicated		68 F	1200 F
Ferritic										
405	2700–2790	0.28	0.11	....	....	6.0	6.2 (1600 F)	Magnetic	61.0	....
430	2600–2750	0.28	0.11	....	....	5.6	6.6 (1500 F)	Magnetic	60.0	....
442	2600–2750	0.28	0.11	12.5	14.2	5.6	....	Magnetic	64.0	....
446	2550–2750	0.27	0.12	12.1	14.1	5.6	....	Magnetic	67.0	113.0
630	2540–2625	0.28	0.11	10.3	13.1	6.6	7.3 (900 F)	Magnetic	77.0	....
631	2590–2640	0.28	....	9.7	12.2	5.7	6.9 (800 F)	Magnetic when hardened	83.0	....
632	2590–2640	0.28	....	9.5	12.2	5.0	6.1 (1000 F)		83.0	....
633	2500–2550	0.28	....	8.9	12.2	6.3	7.0 (1500 F)		79.0	....
634	2500–2550	0.28	....	9.2	12.0	6.4	6.7 (1500 F)		76.0	....

(a) Magnetic permeability is given for annealed material and for a magnetizing force, H, of 200 oersteds.

Note: Physical properties may change with heat-treatment.

Index

A